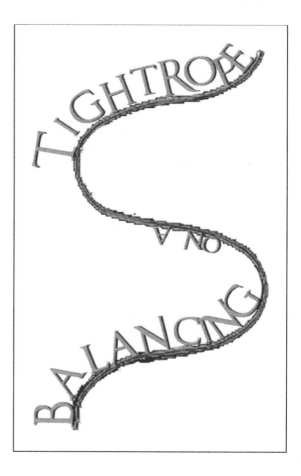

Balancing on a Tightrope:
My Life with Bipolar Disorder

Rand L. Kannenberg

Dedication

Dedicated to Tricia, my wife of forty years because she understands "...in good times and in bad, in sickness and in health...for better, for worse..." far more than anyone else as demonstrated by her dealing with my mental illnesses including Bipolar Disorder.

In Memoriam

In memory of lives lost due to suicide, victims of COVID-19, and casualties of systemic racial injustice (in support of the Black Lives Matter movement).

Introduction

Balancing the ups and downs of Bipolar Disorder (BD) is different for every patient...including me.

{UP} Hi. I'm Rand (no, not "Randy," "Randall," or "Randolph," and my parents can't remember where they came up with the name. Even (R-Kentucky) U.S. Senator Rand Paul's legal name is "Randal" (sic). But, that's not important here. What I'm focusing on is that like so many people, even some very famous, I am bipolar.

{Down} Can untreated trauma that results in PTSD lead to BD if an individual is already at high risk because of family history? That's the case with me.

{UP} How many people can say their first childhood pet was a raccoon? What an amazing first, best friend. I will tell you about Bandit and how I lost her.

{DOWN} Suicide attempts are sadly far too common, and I've had my share. Even in the darkest days, I was still here, and I made it through.

What relationship does anxiety or obsessive-compulsive behavior have with bipolar? They *can* coexist or co-occur. And they do with me.

In this autobiography, I'll share the ups and downs of balancing on the tightrope of mental illness and explain how I've learned to exist and *survive*.

Preface

The Tightrope

According to the National Institute of Mental Health (NIMH), approximately three percent of Americans are diagnosed with BD. Four different types of BD exist. The first two are commonly referred to as Bipolar I Disorder and Bipolar II Disorder. I have the first diagnosis, which is severe episodes of major depression and full-blown mania. Bipolar II Disorder is a severe major depression with "hypomania" only. There are two more possible diagnoses: Cyclothymic Disorder (symptoms do not meet bipolar criteria), and BD, not otherwise specified (NOS).

The average reduction in life expectancy for persons with either form of bipolar is 15 years. Coming from someone who recently celebrated his 60th birthday and whose parents are still alive at ages 85 and 90, where does that put me? I enjoy being sixty. I'm a survivor.

Thirty years of experience working in the field of mental health, and I'm ready to share my story. Taking advantage of being hypomanic, I had a part-time private practice, I evaluated patients 40 hours a week at three emergency departments as part of a hospital chain, and I traveled extensively to present at conventions, seminars, and workshops...I've done it all.

I want to share my stories to empower people diagnosed with mental illness(es) and let you know that you can survive too. This book is also intended for family members, providers, and students. In the pages that follow we'll dive deep into the depths of my diagnoses, share stories of my youth, my career and explore the ups and downs of balancing on the tightrope of BD. We will jump into hard topics at the lowest of lows and the lighthearted, happier topics at the highs.

I want to tell my story so that others know they are not alone. BD is not always a cut and dry, black and white diagnosis. For me there is a lot of grey area. And specifically in my case it's accompanied by other mental illnesses. I'm ready to share the ups and downs with you.

Ready to walk the tightrope with me?

Chapter One

Memories of Phoenix

My Mother told me stories of Duke, the Boxer my parents had when I was a very young child. Is it strange to have memories manifested by stories told to you? The story that stands out in my head was that of a protector, and though I know I don't have the memory, I've manifested the play in my head and can picture myself in the scene.

We were still living in Phoenix, Arizona at the time, where we stayed until I was about five years old. When I was a few years younger, I was playing outside in the yard while my Mother watched from the window. Duke's continual barks alerted her to come out and see what the matter was as I sat ideally by and did nothing. What she found when she arrived at my side was Duke warding off a scorpion through his barks and protective stance. Sadly, Duke died before I could remember him.

Scorpions are common in Arizona, though I don't remember actually seeing one there myself, we moved before I had too many memories of that time in my life. To a small child, a scorpion sting would have not only been traumatic but could have been lethal. To this day, I'm still thankful for Duke, even though I don't really remember him.

In between our house and the neighbor's stood a large cactus that I once got tangled up in so well that the neighbor had to take pliers to pull out the needles stuck in my scalp. He could hear me wailing and, like my mother, came outside to see what the matter was. Mom held me that day as the kind neighbor pulled each needle out one at a time. It tore the skin on my head and I still to this day experience déjà vu when I see a prickly plant of the sorts. My mind transports me back to Phoenix fifty-five years ago when I got into a fight with a cactus.

I was the eldest of three children, born in Phoenix, Arizona. Herman, my dad, fought in the Korean War and went into the painting and drywall business upon his return to The States. My mother, Nancy, worked at a doctor's office as a receptionist. Their fields of employment were crucial to my dreams and desires as they mentored my drive to run my own business, plus work in human services and health care.

A memory of Phoenix that is very clear in my mind was a day I was in school. My father had received a promotion at work and we were in the process of relocating to Denver, Colorado. My parents had already sold the house, so we lived in an apartment not far from school until it was time to move.

In kindergarten one day, I was outside on the playground during recess and very distinctly remember hearing the siren of an emergency vehicle wailing past the school. Even as a young boy, the event struck me, and I knew that something had happened to my sister Kelly. My teacher scooped me up in her arms and tried to comfort me, despite my best protests. I kept kicking her. Not long after, my mother called the school and said she'd be picking me up early as Kelly was in an accident at the apartment.

I just knew…

Looking back, there are only two explanations. I was psychic (as if I even believe in the possibility of being clairvoyant), or I was psychotic (which can be a feature of BD).

Kelly and a neighbor boy were playing in the laundry room of the apartment complex. A maintenance man had stored a plastic bucket of gasoline left from an old lawnmower in the room. I could only imagine he had intentions to come back and retrieve it, so as not to waste it, but somehow it turned over. The gas spilled across the floor to the water heater and caught fire.

Luckily, Kelly was okay. To this day, she has no scarring, other than the horrible memory. That, my friends, is just one reason why gasoline is meant to only go in proper containers. Doing things the right way is something I more than understand because of my "black and white thinking."

Chapter Two

Kids Will Be Kids

Our Phoenix house sat on a hilltop and had a long driveway. One day, Kelly and I took our red wagon to the top of the hill by the house and decided to take a ride. We got in the wagon, she in the front and me in the back, and took off speeding down the hill.

As kids do, we were not thinking about how we would stop at the bottom.

Though neither of us was badly hurt, we had our share of scrapes and skinned knees and elbows.

I often wonder how different life would be if little events like these took a turn for the worse. We were lucky that our crash didn't result in serious injuries. Were these events the beginning scenarios of the ups and downs that would become my life?

One time Kelly and I took a little stroll down our street to a stand set up on the corner. The man was selling ducklings and we bought a pair. We named them Donald and Daisy, of course, and took them home to swim in the bathtub. It has escaped my memory of how a young boy such as myself would acquire money to purchase a duck, much less two ducks, but I must have had some kind of allowance or the merchant gave them to us for free.

What happened to those ducks? I do not know. What I do know is they did not stay at our house for long. Perhaps Father put them outside and they waddled away to a nearby body of water. I like to think they thrived and became happy ducks that lived a long life.

Chapter Three

My First Loss

RAND KANNENBERG AND MASCOT 'BANDIT'

Fuzz-Faced Critter Red Hot Soccer Fan

Denver was a breath of fresh air when we finally said goodbye to Phoenix, literally one extreme to the other in terms of climate. Not long after being there, our new veterinarian asked us to take in a baby raccoon (a kit) and nurse it until it could be returned to the wild. The mother had been found dead at the side of a road in the mountains and this kit, along with other members of the litter in the nest or den, were alive but in need of TLC.

17

We named the one that we were given Bandit. I don't believe it was illegal in the 60s to have a wild animal for a pet, if it was, nobody seemed to care.

While I don't remember Duke, as I was too young, I most definitely remember Bandit. I never had a dog or a cat of my own and did not discount the fact that it was a very unique situation to have a raccoon.

When she was small enough to be held in the palm of my hand, I found an old baby doll that had a toy bottle. I was able to clean it up and use it to feed her milk and she eventually got stronger and stronger. She depended on me for nutrition and looking back, as silly as it sounds, it was caring for Bandit that helped prepare me to be a parent. Once she was old enough, we were able to switch her to wet dog food, milk, and a raw egg, and it was my responsibility to feed her daily.

One evening, I was preparing Bandit's dinner and cut my finger on the lid to the metal can. Within days, I had an infection in the cut finger. The next week I developed a life-threatening condition called sepsis, an infection that is body-wide, and was admitted to the hospital. What a traumatic event for a young boy!

Raccoons tend to have bad reputations and humans think they carry rabies, which some definitely may but not all. Turns out, a metal dog food can could be just as lethal. We never had to worry about Bandit being rabid or getting other diseases.

The only one of the family she didn't care for was my father, despite the niceties he did for her. He built her a beautiful cage outside that was big enough for her to have her own shelf to lay on and a large tree branch where she could climb up and down. When he'd go fishing, he'd bring back spoils for her. If he was successful and brought home trout, Bandit would eat like a royal. I think she held a grudge against my father though, as he was the one who always ended her fun at nighttime and took her outside to her cage for bed.

Bandit was so creative. She would sit in the kitchen and use her little hands to unscrew a jar of peanut butter. The kids at my school and their parents would come to visit her and spend time with her almost like she was an attraction. My soccer team made her the mascot. She even had her own uniform! Admittedly, my pet raccoon was definitely more popular than me.

Behind our home, my parents owned half of the irrigation ditch. There was a beautiful tree on top with a rope swing where we'd quickly swing back and forth, one side to the other. Up and down.

We had to keep Bandit away from this area and away from the dogs because they would attack her. If you didn't know, raccoons can drown a dog by holding its head underwater, so that was a worry as well that she could possibly turn on one if they attacked her.

Trees were to be avoided too. She'd climb to the top of a tree and make camp. I remember us having to call 911 once because she was stuck at the top and none of our ladders would reach. The fireman went up to the top and rescued our Bandit.

Sadly, Bandit started to become aggressive as she got older, returning to her natural instincts. The veterinarian said this was normal, of course, and the only way to deal with it was to let her go. We drove thirty minutes from our home and released her back into nature. I left all of her remaining dog food there, hoping she'd have a place to come back to and she'd be fed, for a little while anyway.

Letting go of Bandit was very hard for me. She was really the first loss I ever experienced.

My second crisis came a short time later. The five of us went to Estes Park, Colorado at the entrance to Rocky Mountain National Park. We rented a cabin at the same lodge where we went every summer. Usually, Bandit would go with us as

I walked her on a dog leash. It was bad enough that she wasn't with us. I just knew I'd be miserable during the trip and tried my hardest to put it out of my mind.

But the real stressor came after we arrived back home. We had been burglarized! All of our belongings were removed from the dresser drawers and thrown on the floor. We couldn't even feel safe in our own home. And, I felt dirty. This definitely affected me then and still does to this day.

Chapter Four

The Scent of Childhood

A little suburb of Denver called Golden, was where we played our home soccer games. There was (and still is) a Coors brewery nearby (now known as "Molson Coors Beverage Company,") and you could smell the hops and the barley from a mile away.

Wheat Ridge, another suburb about the same distance from our house as Golden, had a Jolly Rancher factory. As a kid, *that* was the smell of euphoria. I would wake up every morning and smell the scent of the day. Cherry was my favorite, both in candy and the smell. The scents were so distinct.

At the time, Jolly Rancher flavors were apple, "fire stix," orange tangerine, lemon, grape, peach, sour apple, cherry, blue raspberry, grape, green apple, and watermelon.

As kids, it was common to take a school field trip to tour the factory. Walking up and down the floors in groups of twenty, we'd watch the glassy sheen of the candy as it was poured from container to mold and then wrapped individually.

Cherry days were the best days to visit.

I can still smell the "fragrance" of Coors as an adult when we go by. Sadly, the Jolly Rancher factory is no more. When Hershey bought the company, it closed and Jolly Rancher production was moved to the existing Hershey plants in Pennsylvania.

It was around this time in my life I remember working with my father in his home office. Even as a child, I was impressed by his ability to work on his own. He trusted me, a ten-year-old boy, to use his typewriter and type out an invoice when a job was done. I'd be extra careful and once complete; I'd address the envelope using the typewriter as well.

In Denver, my mother worked as a student aide (not a teacher aide), where she would take notes for disabled students who were unable to write. She'd also help them complete their coursework and exams. Later she worked with toddlers and children doing hearing and vision screenings at the county department of health and environment. Mother's jobs working with the toddlers, children, youth, and the disabled made me excited inside and I wanted to do that too.

My childhood home (with my dad as the general contractor) was in the Denver suburb of Lakewood, where the cherry Jolly Rancher smells would waft in my bedroom window. This portion of my youth gave me ambition. And these familiar smells still transport me back to childhood.

Chapter Five

President of Elementary School

In my Lakewood elementary school, I was president of the student government and my first kiss was with Karen. I gave her a ring from a candy machine, and she might as well have been my First Lady. Oh, how childhood innocence is special. Even with Karen being my girlfriend, I "played around" with other kids my age or a year or two younger and older. This may have been an early indicator of Pediatric Bipolar Disorder (PBD), a controversial diagnosis with some, but I endorse it.

A later girlfriend, Michelle and I got into a fight because, at the student talent show, she sang a song called "Monster Mash" by Bobby "Boris" Pickett. I thought her singing was too loud. But I liked her mother. She filled their house with photographs of her as a trick water skier, standing on the shoulders of others. Sadly, things didn't work out with Michelle (or her mom) in elementary school and I snuck a kiss with Sally, a neighbor girl who was my age. (Since you already know my wife's name is Tricia, you can go ahead and assume correctly that Sally and I parted ways too.)

There was a teacher in elementary school who would smack my fingers with a ruler because she thought I wasn't holding my pencil correctly. As you can imagine, this made me very angry. Why was this form of punishment acceptable?

While misbehaving wasn't typical for me, I got into a terrible argument with the principal over whether or not the bookstore needed to sell large erasers.

I said yes.

He said no.

Up and down.

Can you picture an eleven-year-old boy trying to take a stand for what he believes as a towering man crushes that dream? It was likely not that dramatic, but I got so upset that he spanked me with a paddle. Back in those days, it was common for a principal to keep a paddle in his office for the punishment of unruly children. I knew many who suffered from its wooden chastisement.

My mother did not approve of corporal punishment from a non parent and pulled me from that school. I transferred to another school for the second half of sixth grade.

The true punishment may have been making me go to what we referred to as the "school without walls." The alternative school was nothing more than a room with portable barriers to separate the different classes, which weren't of much use at all and certainly not capable of keeping noise out. Here, I did my best to fit in but sought relief when summer came, and I knew I'd be heading to a different school.

Again, up and down.

Was this difficulty with early relationships and controlling and regulating my temper and mood a sign of PBD?

Chapter Six

Busying Myself in Junior High

Middle school was called junior high back then and was a time in my life where I easily busied myself. I dated Norma. I was the master of ceremonies for the student talent show, a downhill ski racer, and ran the mile, breaking the school record at five minutes and two seconds.

I organized a "kidnapping" of sorts for the teachers...the principal approved, of course, we didn't really kidnap them. Students' parents picked up the teachers and drove them to my house where my mother served lunch. As an adult, I look back on this and hope the gesture was enjoyed. Even teachers need a break every once in a while. But I wonder now who took care of the school and all of the remaining students.

I had a decreased need for sleep in junior high, excessive energy, excitement, and goal orientation. These are early signs of PBD which can occur between the ages of five and 18.

It didn't help that my voice hadn't fully changed, and I was taking choir. The sounds that came out of my mouth could rival Peter Brady during puberty. My music teacher even suggested I open my mouth, but not actually sing.

Todd C. was my best friend in junior high. Even though we were fierce competitors on the track, we managed to stay friends through cutthroat races. We'd take turns, placing first and second, accidentally cutting each other with our cleats as we zoomed down the track lanes.

Todd C.'s dad owned a compact car, the first one that I had ever been in. The family also had a "wild" dog in their backyard that I found interesting. These were new experiences for me.

My competitive nature didn't end with Todd. My youngest sibling, my brother Scott, and I would go at it from time to time. He was throwing darts in our basement one night and tossed one my way, piercing my ear. I didn't let that slide though. I got him back, even if it was merely an accident when we were playing in the back of my dad's pickup truck. I sprayed a chemical in the air and it wafted toward him, getting in his eyes. Though he was not the intended target, revenge was sweet. My mother was probably more upset with me than Scott, truth be told.

Like me, my brother had mental health issues. Some of which didn't manifest until he was an adult, but nonetheless, they were there. He excelled in sports...track, baseball, basketball, football. At nine-years-old, he broke the national record by kicking a thirty-five-yard field goal. His photo and story appeared in Sports Illustrated magazine and he garnered national attention.

At times, usually in the bathroom, Scott and I were goofy with one another. We would say, "I wrote this song just for you," and then sing a short tune that we made up. Sometimes we would include Kelly. Scott and I also started the phrase "don't hop too hard," when the other person said, "hopping in," before getting in the shower. The funny thing is that Tricia and I have continued this tradition.

Kelly was the middle sibling, and she and I would make fun of Scott, calling him "buck teeth," because he desperately needed braces. When he ate, he'd make an irritating noise by scraping the inside of his mouth with a fork or a spoon. Even decades later, I can still hear that sound.

Scott and I shared bunk beds. I slept on the top and Scott slept on the bottom. My brother had a horrible habit of smearing his boogers on the wall. Mom made him clean them off. And, he was almost impossible to wake up in the mornings. Definitely a night owl, it took my mother many tries and a long time to get him to fully wake up and start the day. As someone who began working in the mental health field, I've wondered about his lack of energy and how that played a role in his depression and his own struggles with BD.

My first hunting trip was in 1974. I was 14 years old and my father took me out with a friend of his. We went out early one morning to go deer hunting. I had just received my Hunter's Safety Card. I shot and killed a record four-point buck that morning. The photograph of me with the buck appeared on the front page of the Denver Post's sports section.

This experience was traumatic for me.

I never wanted to kill anything. Taking the life of a big and beautiful animal who was defenseless against my rifle and skilled shot. Not only was I bothered by killing the animal, the three of us had to transport it back to the truck. The deer weighed nearly 350 pounds and my father and his friend had to cut it into three sections and drag it for at least a mile or more until we reached the truck. It was very hard work for me.

I did not want to hunt after that day, but I also didn't want to disappoint my father. I'd join him on goose and pheasant hunting trips in my teen years. We also fished once in a while. He was an avid fisherman and we'd take long trips to new destinations up into the mountains of Colorado and Wyoming. Sometimes we would spend hours in the car with my father driving, we would fish until dark, and then return home. I'd be exhausted and would curl up on the floorboard of the truck or our El Camino and rest my head on the passenger's seat until I fell asleep, safe with my Father at the wheel.

Chapter Seven

High on High School

I was full of energy in high school. One summer job I had then was working at a private pool's snack bar and front desk. That was my mentality, always working, plenty of energy. An adult family friend told me that I was "overactive and just trying to get attention," but I just thought I was a normal teenager.

That pool was one of the largest outdoor pools in the country. It was round with an island, three diving boards in the middle and a wading pool surrounded by a sandy beach area. It was so big;

they couldn't keep it heated properly and the water was always cold. Patrons were often unable to swim comfortably until they got used to it. I remember making announcements over the public address (PA) system. Several times a day I would say, "Attention. Attention. It is now time for adult swim. All those 16 years of age and younger must leave the pool at this time." It always made me nervous to make the announcements, but at the same time it was exhilarating.

I continued running in high school, cross country specifically and broke another record in distance at ten minutes and 32 seconds. A sweet reward is this record cannot be broken as they have changed the distance in cross country from two to three miles, so my record will always stand.

A ski racing accident halted my sports participation as I tore the cartilage in my right knee and had to have surgery to repair it. Scars have never healed well for me and this was back in the day when surgeons made long incisions. I still have the half-moon scar today.

At the same age, I had high fevers and severe abdominal pain. Though all the tests came back normal, my doctors opted to do exploratory surgery and found my appendix was seriously enlarged, so that was removed. The surgeon had not thought the appendix could be the cause of the pain and my primary care physician (PCP) diagnosed me with Familial Mediterranean Fever (FMF), even though I didn't have that family or ethnic history, which is common in most cases. Still have that scar too.

I had three platonic girlfriends in high school, nothing really happened but quick kisses with those three. They kept my attention but weren't love matches. I knew Tricia in high school too, but we never dated then. She was my sounding board when I had relationship troubles and she'd give me advice. Spoiler alert, I'd later make the decision to cut out the middleman, so to speak, and just date and marry her. One of my best decisions, hands down, was to marry Tricia. But I'll share more details about that later.

As kids, my siblings and I regularly traumatized our babysitters. It was always a different one because my parents could rarely get a babysitter to sit for us more than once. When I was in high school, we had a babysitter named Lorraine who watched over Kelly and Scott. I was really too old at the time to need a babysitter and might have even been working as a busboy that evening and unable to watch them myself.

That night she was at our house while my parents were out late. She had put my siblings to bed, and it was just the two of us awake. She came on to me and we kissed for what seemed like all night. She was already an adult, likely 20 or 21 years old if memory serves me right and I was a mere 16. It was the first time I had ever made it to second base with a girl.

Her father was a prominent figure in our community. Now, I think back and wonder how many other boys she did that with on a whim. Our age difference likely violated consent laws too, not that I would have realized that at the time. Oddly enough, I don't remember ever seeing her again.

Another time in high school, former U.S. Senator William "Bill" Armstrong (R-Colorado) invited me to meet and pray with him. He offered me an internship at his D.C. office and a military academy nomination, both of which I declined (politely of course), and instead chose to discuss world events with the senator.

Later I had a private tour of the White House and a meeting at the Old Executive Office Building about issues regarding America's youth. I represented my service organization as best as I could and left roses for First Lady Rosalynn Carter. Everyone was very busy walking and working on my tour of The White House. I liked observing the chaos.

My first public speaking opportunity took place at the Fontainebleau Hotel in Miami Beach, Florida. I represented my service organization again for this event and spoke to peers delivering the keynote address at the organization's annual convention.

Even as a teenager I enjoyed giving back, doing projects to help others, and making people happy.

Ups and downs.

My mother helped me piece together a clown outfit from clothes that were too big for me. I borrowed makeup from Keith and his father who both dressed up as clowns from time to time, and the two of us would go to Oktoberfest in Denver and *clown around.* The smiles were the best part.

Some say they've had bad experiences with clowns, and while I know that must be true, I never had any myself. I would go into the special education school dressed up with my clown makeup just so and make the children so happy with my visits. I was a volunteer clown with disabled youth for several years.

At school, I made the morning announcements on the PA for the administration. I was appointed to this position because the front office staff liked me, the best student I was, and I felt like it was an honor to be recruited to such a position.

Sometimes I played music while talking; I liked how my voice sounded. Tricia later told me that students threw wads of paper at the speaker mounted to the wall in the classroom while I talked and would "boo" me. This was a surprise because I was set up in the principal's office when I did the announcements. I had no clue whatsoever my peers were so horrible. I thought of this just like I did being a clown: I was entertaining. I was able to put on a show and thought my announcements were enjoyable. I easily walked the tightrope in high school.

I was called to the principal's office on a regular basis, but not because I was in trouble. It was that favorite child syndrome. The principal often consulted with me for help on projects like rewriting school policies and procedures. I wouldn't tell my friends for fear of embarrassment or teacher's pet teasing. I didn't want them to know I was seen differently by our teachers and especially the principal.

I visited Spain while in high school as a foreign exchange student. The teenager who hosted me in Barcelona traveled to the United States later that year and stayed with me and my family. It was an eye-opening experience to travel and see other parts of the world. The culture and wonders of the things I saw while I was there will always be with me.

I was a sophomore at the time, but even at a young age, I wasn't scared to be abroad and away from home. In Barcelona, there were green trucks and jeeps that carried military men, standing on the backs of the tailgates holding onto the bars of the vehicles. They carried automatic weapons and were still very controlling to keep the order. This was part of the painful transition from a dictatorship to a democratic monarchy in Spain. Despite the presence of the soldiers, I didn't feel unsafe, but it was a very interesting thing to witness in another country and at such an impressionable age.

On that trip, our high school group went to a topless nightclub. I don't remember if we had to show an ID card. We were also able to drink alcohol in Spain if sixteen or older. In addition to drinking in bars and restaurants, we would drink at the homes where we were staying during lunch and dinner alike. I was sick for three weeks after returning home from that trip. My pediatrician blamed my illness on the excessive alcohol at such a young age, saying I might be "allergic" to it. Traveling to Spain was the first of several trips abroad.

I got migraines fairly regularly in my late teens and they have continued throughout my life. According to the National Institutes of Health (NIH), up to 25 percent of patients with migraines have comorbid BD. And also from the NIH, nearly 20 percent of bipolar patients have asthma, and poor cholesterol levels. Both of these additional diagnoses are true in my case.

In the beginning, I had bipolar symptoms and didn't know it, and was diagnosed with debilitating migraine headaches at the age of 18. I was prescribed an antidepressant for migraines, which I still take. The good news is that three new medications were approved by the FDA in 2018. They are the first drugs that address frequency, intensity, and duration of migraines.

My first depressive episode happened at age 17 after I returned home from a funeral for a 16-year-old friend who died of muscular dystrophy. His two brothers also passed away of the same disease between the ages of 13 and 16. As a teenager, experiencing death generally comes with losing people close to you who are older. Losing a peer was a very hard thing to bear at the time.

My first suicidal gesture occurred the night of his funeral. I waited for my family to go to bed and took three aspirin tablets, a shot of whiskey, and put a belt around my neck. Was this cry for help another sign of PBD? It may have been, but until now, I have never told a soul about this secret. I did not want to kill myself. I was signaling that there was a problem. I was truly down.

Chapter Eight

Fast Cars and Freedom

I got into my share of trouble as a teenager, usually by association and not of my own doing. My first car was a 1959 Plymouth Sports Fury. I later bought a Cutlass from a stranger and another Oldsmobile from my parents, but the Fury was the first and my favorite. Todd C. and I would rowdy up some trouble with a revolving yellow light we had that would plug into the cigarette lighter. We'd set it up on the top of the dashboard and successfully pull cars over to the side of the road. We never approached them, just waited for them to pull over and pass them as if we were on our way somewhere important. Nowadays, impersonating a police officer is a serious crime.

There was a roadway seldom used between Boulder and Golden where we'd take the Fury to speed race. We would easily hit 85 miles per hour, if not faster. The speed was exhilarating and we both got an adrenaline rush from the experience. The Fury was one of those cars that held true to the saying, "It was only used by an old lady to go to church on Sundays." At least until I got my hands on it. It had a push-button gear shift on the dash, electric windows and seats, and a double wingtip in the rear. People would refer to it as The Batmobile and I loved every minute of it.

Having the responsibility of a car meant I needed a job to pay for things like gas and insurance. I'd work afternoons, evenings, or weekends as a busboy at a restaurant not too far from my home. One night, an adult waitress who also worked there approached me and said she wanted the two of us to have sex in the cooler. I was a 16-year-old boy. Can you imagine the restraint? I was very attracted to her and the possibility turned me on until I worried about getting fired. I needed my job, after all.

I worked at a paint store after I left my job at the restaurant. This specific store was a chain and I'd go on to work at several locations throughout my college years as well. It was steady work and I did a good job.

I had two other good friends in high school, oddly enough also named Todd. Todd B. and Todd A. weren't in the same circles as Todd C., so I hung out with them on separate occasions. Todd B's mother was an alcoholic and because of that, we would see fire trucks and emergency vehicles at their house pretty often.

Todd A.'s mother was an amazing Italian cook and I always enjoyed being invited over to their house for dinner.

Many times, the two Todd's would spend the night at my house. We would sneak down to the basement while being very quiet and smoke cigars after everyone went to bed. Looking back, I wish I knew where we got those cigars. We also would sneak out of the house and streak down the street in my neighborhood. Nowadays, that would be called indecent exposure, a sex crime. Luckily in my day, most people were already asleep in their beds in the wee hours of the morning when we ran naked on West 16th Place.

When another friend, Keith, would stay over or we had downtime after school in the afternoons, we would get into all sorts of trouble. We would get the house phone when nobody was around, or when they were all asleep, and he would make prank calls to our school teachers. This was back in the days before caller ID became a thing and landlines were common.

In Colorado, skiing was a popular pastime when I was a kid, still is of course, but I distinctly remember a time when Keith got the two of us in trouble when we were riding a bus that drove members of a club up to the ski area. He was careful, but not careful enough because he still got caught throwing orange peels and hitting the driver in the back of the head. At a Boy Scout meeting, he started a fire in the trash can inside the men's restroom. His tact got us both in trouble, per usual, as I was guilty by association and kicked out of Scouts, just like Keith. He's now a firefighter and I dare say I bet he did not disclose this arson incident during his interview process.

There were two things that I missed after Keith and I spent less time together. First, the sandwiches his mother would make...cucumbers and peanut butter. We did not know about healthy eating habits in my family. Secondly, horses! Their property was zoned to allow horses and I loved going over there.

I decided to organize Senior Ditch Day, where dozens of taxi cabs took us seniors to City Park and the zoo during the school day. I had to get the idea approved by the school and as long as no one got hurt or there wasn't any damage to property, they agreed to my plan.

I asked everyone to dress like an international tourist for the occasion. I was supposed to look like a Frenchman with my costume consisting of a leather jacket (that ironically, I bought in Spain), a beret, and a hand-drawn mustache I made myself with my black clown makeup. I remember spending the day at the zoo with Tricia and our mutual friend, Anna. Some seniors played pranks by taking for sale signs from nearby homes and placing them in front of the school. Such mischief would be against the law in today's age.

This time in history was before the Department of Health, Education, and Welfare (HEW) issued Title IX. We used to call girls sweethearts. I didn't feel the term as sexist at the time, but more of a compliment. One of my girlfriends, Jodi, hated the title. The pet name went away when Title IX was issued.

I was with *a sweetheart* from our local school chapter of my service organization at the CU/Boulder Folsom Field for a Beach Boys concert. She used her tongue when kissing me. While I had no clue what she was "doing to me," I liked it, despite being a bit confused.

At another concert, I escorted a group of disabled kids to see Donny and Marie Osmond. We were able to go backstage to meet the performers. My, what a treat it was to see Marie in her dressing room in front of all those round lights. She only had one button clasped on her top and I couldn't help but want all of her attention. The kids got her attention instead, but I could only stare at her.

Despite all the trouble with the Toms and Keith and the fun of Senior Ditch Day, I was the graduating male chosen to give the commencement address at my high school graduation, an honor to this day.

A major up.

Chapter Nine

The Edge of Adulthood

Like the ups and downs of BD, there were ups and downs with skiing too. You can come very close when you're doing the mile run or cross country, but when you're doing a giant slalom or downhill race, you're not even a second behind the person in front of you.

I was a Class C skier, but I was not far away from the people two levels above me. I only raced in junior high school. I worked with the local Boys and Girls Club chapter when I went to The Colorado College (CC) and instructed skiing lessons sometimes in the afternoons. The Broadmoor Hotel had a ski area behind their location in Colorado Springs, and we would ski in really tough conditions. It was very icy because of man-made snow.

I attended CC for a year and a half after high school graduation. I was deathly afraid of what they called their "block plan." Essentially students took the same class for three and a half weeks before moving onto the next.

I did not do well taking German with this method of teaching and learning. I found myself struggling again with Geology as the required memorization was intense. We went on field trips and had to recognize the name of each object and it was extremely stressful. I remember the night before that final exam I bought a bottle of cough syrup and drank all of it. I was so sick that I spent the night at the Student Health Center and was given an incomplete for the class the next day because I missed the test.

The NIMH reports that a sign of PBD manifesting itself at an early age (5 to 18 years) can be suicidal or self-harm behaviors. I was not suicidal. I didn't want to die because of these stressors. I was simply willing to make myself ill to accomplish a goal when I became depressed about something going on in my life. I was hopeless and helpless. Until now, I have never told anyone about this behavior.

Ups and downs.

I was not a good standardized test taker. Though when I first applied to CC (the "Harvard of the West") I was accepted, it was not based on my test scores; my extracurricular activities were what made my application stand out. I had not excelled on the ACT and SAT. Being president of many organizations and my involvement in other activities throughout my high school career helped seal the deal. This involvement in activities outside my schoolwork continued throughout my college career.

I played an active role on campus politically. For example, I led a peaceful rally in support of the diplomats and other Americans held hostage by radical students in the U.S. Embassy in Tehran, Iran. The following year or two, I participated in anti-Rocky Flats Nuclear Power Plant protests. I was inspired by Saint Mother Teresa, Reverend Martin Luther King, Jr., and attorney Mahatma Gandhi. I don't think I was ever afraid of standing up for what I believed in, rather things like that Geology final exam and dealing with the loss of a peer weighed on me heavily.

Good and bad things alike happened while I was at CC.

I made enough extra money at the paint store in Colorado Springs to send my parents on a vacation for their 25th anniversary. I paid for roundtrip airfare to California, a stay at a luxury hotel, and spending money. Both Kelly and Scott promised to pay their share, but they never did.

I would call home and be talking to my Mom when I heard noises in the background. Scott was knocking my Dad to the ground. My Mother told me not to, but I called the Lakewood Police Department 75 miles away from where I was.

This behavior with Scott continued for years.

Tricia and I were still dating despite attending different schools. She attended the University of Colorado in Boulder, where I later transferred. In Lakewood, Colorado, on a warm sunny day in June,

I married Tricia. Our friendship had blossomed into much more when we realized we wanted to be together. I was twenty years old and she was nineteen. Over 350 people attended our wedding at my parents' church. One beautiful thing about our relationship is that together we were able to grow into adults.

Once we were married, both sets of parents collectively decided that since we were old enough to be married, we were old enough to pay for our college education. So she and I got straight to work in addition to our studies. It made learning harder trying to hold down jobs, pay bills for our new apartment, and just figuring out how to be adults. Aside from the few months we had lived in dorm rooms in college, she and I had never lived away from our parents' homes. This was all new to us and I'm thankful we were able to do it side by side.

Like all relationships, Tricia and I had our ups and downs. Being married so young, I think my "seven-year itch" came that first year. I was attracted to another woman and for this alone I was banned by our nondenominational Christian youth group. And then, I projected my issues onto Tricia and even accused her of being attracted to the manager at the jewelry store where she worked. Wrongly accused, most definitely. I had a lot of maturing to do.

For the second time in my life, I purchased ducklings. This time as a gift for each other for Easter. Tricia and I named them Donald and Daisy (sound familiar?). Perhaps our duck-naming skills were unoriginal, but it was cute and fun to enjoy the ducklings with my new wife. We let them play in the bathtub for a bit of time before we took them to a nearby lake, setting them free to go on and live what we hoped would be a long life.

Shortly after we were married, Tricia lost her wedding ring and was devastated. It really upset her because one of the diamonds came from a ring of my grandmother's. There were diamonds that were split up and given to the grandchildren, including me.

The very same time, we were looking for a small dog, all the while knowing that pets were not allowed in our apartment complex. In the afternoon I was to find a dog to adopt, I found Tricia's ring underneath our bed.

I went out and I bought a poodle/beagle mix to join our family and came back to the apartment ahead of Tricia to surprise her when she got home. I put the diamond ring on the collar around the puppy's neck. She came home to find our new addition, MacKenzie, with an even bigger surprise of getting her wedding ring back. I was so glad to give her the good news. We moved shortly thereafter because our lease was about to expire and as you can probably tell, I'm a rule follower.

I went back to work for the paint store chain, but this time at the Boulder location. This was the third job for the same company. Two things happened here, and both were early signs of BD-a manic episode with psychotic features.

At the paint store, I became obsessed with a fellow employee's illegal behavior. Along with others, I witnessed him stealing money from the cash register. In addition to this misconduct, he used the store's back parking lot as a meeting spot for drug deals.

I judged others who were engaged in illegal activity and I reported what I saw regarding both crimes to the police. The officers came to the store, questioned me and other employees involved, and spoke to the store manager. They decided not to press any charges, which greatly upset me. I locked myself to a shelf in the store with my bike lock. I eventually agreed to unlock myself but was extremely upset that justice would not be served. That same day I had paranoid delusions. I heard clicking noises on the store's phone and thought it was being wire-tapped.

As previously mentioned, in high school, I was given access to Rosalynn Carter, the First Lady, and talked to Bill Armstrong, the senator, but there were still issues that I felt were unresolved by the time I got to college. I started a national group called The President's Committee on American Youth and Young Adults. We recruited people to join. I was the chairman and Tricia, though she hated every minute of it, was the vice-chairman. We had to use our mailing address at our apartment to register the group.

Not long after, we received a letter from the chief counsel at The White House issuing a cease and desist order about continued use of the presidential seal/emblem. I was so young. I had no clue that was a federal offense. They never approved the committee and we agreed to discontinue use of the symbol on our business cards and stationery.

This is really another example of bipolar mania. I was taking a full load of classes and working, I did not have leftover time to devote to this not-for-profit agency. It ate up all my free time and I was forced to get up early and do things where I could. There was pretty good press coverage in both Denver newspapers, and one writer said I was a "ruby-faced young man." I still remember that remark.

Sadly, we did not accomplish any of our goals, we shot ourselves in the foot by using the emblem without White House approval. We disbanded.

In 1982, I received my Bachelor of Arts degree, with Distinction, in Political Science and Sociology from UC Denver (UCD), and my Master of Arts degree, Sociology in 1984 (Thesis: "Political Socialization and Resocialization of American Youth and Young Adults: The Process of Learning,

Unlearning, and Relearning Political Norms, Values, Attitudes, and Behaviors.") from UCD. I was both a Sociology teaching and research assistant. This was and still is a nonconventional education in the mental health field because Sociology is the scientific study of groups and societies. Most of my peers at my first post-graduate job were psychologists or social workers.

After I graduated, Tricia and I moved to Austin, Texas, so she could pursue her Master's degree in Speech Language Pathology. My Uncle Larry, who also is my godfather and was a Licensed Clinical Psychologist (now retired), helped me get a job working at the adult halfway house operated by a community mental health center. A year later, in 1985, I attended Austin Community College where I received a Certificate in "Management and Supervisory Series."

A few months earlier, Tricia's father sent us a letter asking that we please return to the Denver area. He had never written before, so this was very out of character. We were alarmed when we first saw the envelope. The correspondence said that he hoped we hadn't fallen in love with Austin because he wanted to have us live somewhere in Colorado, Tricia's birthplace.

Once Tricia finished her degree, we packed our things and headed back to Denver where we would plant roots and raise our children.

Chapter Ten

Bullies and Underage Inappropriate Situations
(ages 10 to 17 years old)

Elementary school was where I met a bully named Kurt. In fifth grade, he and his friends pushed me down to the ground and pulled down my pants. He didn't touch me, but my best efforts telling them to stop were useless. This wouldn't be the last I'd see of Kurt.

We were back together in junior high and one time he, along with several older boys and myself, were taking showers in the locker room after wrestling practice. Kurt approached me directly and peed on me in the shower. Again, I told him to stop.

When I was working at the paint store in Lakewood, the manager Rachel ("Rach"), said to me, "Rand, you have the face of a woman." The comment she made has never set well with me and really upset my mother. I was not confused with my sexuality and never had any issues with people who were gay or lesbian, which I assumed she was implying, it just wasn't for me. I believe the concept of "bullying" with regards to people like Kurt and Rach has much to do with their sexuality as the perpetrators. Now, as an adult, I wonder if sexual immaturity or confusion were why Kurt bullied me as he did. Rach too.

My junior year in high school, I was elected to the international board of a service organization and traveled almost 20 times to the different states that made up my territory. I made more than a few stops in Coon Rapids, Minnesota. I loved their water tower that was by the high school I was visiting. There's nothing like that in the Denver area.

Everyone really treated me well and wanted to host me in fancy ways since I was high up in the ranks of the club.

At one of several meetings at headquarters, Gregg, the paid adult employee of the group, asked me if I and several of my peers would like to stay in his condominium which was within walking distance of the meeting location.

When I got there, I realized I was the only teenager in the room. I remember him having me lay down on the floor and rubbing lotion on my back. I definitely made it clear that I didn't want him touching me, but I have no memory of what, if anything, happened next.

On another trip in New York City, I saw drugs being bought and sold in Times Square. I was surrounded by litter and prostitution was on every corner.

The same year Derek, the head leader of the local chapter of the adult service organization, traveled from his home and was staying at a hotel near me in Lakewood. He said he wanted us to have a meeting, which made sense because of our elected roles in the organizations and invited me to his room and to stay the night. I did not feel comfortable with this, saying that I had to call my parents. They told me absolutely not. I went home that evening and do not remember what happened before I drove away from his hotel in my Fury.

It wasn't as simple as boys will be boys or bullies will be bullies. Kids and teenagers go through this kind of thing every day and these incidents were the start of many that over the course of my life would really wear me down.

Was I abused by a peer and one or both adults? I personally don't believe in "false memories."

Chapter Eleven

Professional Standards

As a child, I experienced that "emergency intuition" when I heard the ambulance and knew something had happened with Kelly. One morning, as an adult, I had a similar experience. Again, I can't explain how I knew, but I was riding the bus on my way to work and sensed something was very wrong with my grandfather (my mother's father). I knew deep down something was wrong.

When I arrived at the mental health center where I worked in Denver at the time, I made a call to my mother, just to check in and make sure everything was okay. She said no and informed me that my grandfather had been killed in a car accident earlier that morning.

Nobody believed me as a child when I had the feeling something had happened with Kelly, so I

74

didn't dare tell my mother about the experience this time, for fear she wouldn't believe me again.

My job was working for a mental health center's adult outpatient clinic. This is where I inherited a full caseload of male parolees and probationers, who only had to sign in on a clipboard at the reception desk to receive their mandatory treatment. I refused to accept the fact that these clients were getting no treatment, and the Department of Corrections was still paying for mental health treatment for each of them.

I took action by developing a treatment curriculum to address their aggressiveness, breaking rules and laws, carelessness, dishonesty, irritability, indifference, impulsivity, irresponsibility and substance use disorders. I designed the Resocial Group (TM) curriculum to decrease recidivism for offenders with Antisocial Personality Disorder and a coexisting substance abuse or dependence. My evidence-based techniques, first created by me in

1986, are considered sociotherapy or sociological counseling. I had a success rate (crime and drug free for at least one year) of 86 percent! This is unheard of.

I was at the Denver clinic for two years until I was offered a job at the city's oldest and largest not-for-profit inpatient hospital, where I opened a new day treatment program for adults. I was an agency-based therapist for five years (also at several mental health centers in the capacity of manager, or director with a variety of ages and types of populations).

I was licensed in Colorado as an addiction counselor. I was also certified nationally as both a clinical sociologist (in small group therapy), and as a case manager. I was the first male and first non-nurse in Colorado to have five years of full-time paid experience in case management. This qualified me to sit for the written exam, which I passed.

At the end of my career, I saw patients in the emergency departments at three Denver hospitals for five years and for another five years was on the faculty at a city/county training center, two community colleges, one summer school, and two universities where I taught counseling and case management skills. Plus, I was a dotcom owner for two years. For at least 15 years (holding down many jobs at the same time), I was a trainer and speaker at addiction or psychiatric workshops, seminars and conferences. I was the first educator in behavioral health to work in all fifty U.S. states including Alaska, Hawaii and Puerto Rico. I designed seventeen courses popular with mental health and substance abuse counselors and therapists, physicians, nurses and law enforcement officials. The classes were half-day, full-day or two-days in length. Some courses were taught online and some taught in-person and were presented all over the United States.

The titles were:

- "Medication Abuse: Over-the-Counter and Prescription Drug Abuse and Dependence"
- "Sociotherapy for Sociopaths"/"Resocial Group™"
- "Using Humor in Offender Counseling and Supervision"
- "Clinical Case Management and Behavioral Health"
- "Deviance and Criminal Behavior"
- "Theories and Models of Helping Offenders Change"
- "Communication Techniques with Clients"
- "Cultural Diversity Skills in Community Corrections"
- "Addiction Counseling and Professional Ethics"
- "Criminal Offenders with Coexisting Diagnoses" (aka, "Successful Outcomes for Criminal Offenders")

- "Antisocial Personality Disorder & Other Challenging Client Populations"
- "Clinical Case Management in Healthcare and Human Services"
- "Methamphetamine"
- "The Meth Epidemic" (aka, "METH: Assessment, Intervention & Treatment")
- "Clinical Evaluation for Antisocial Personality Disorder and Substance Use Disorders: The Knowledge, Skills and Attitudes to Use Three Screening Instruments"
- "The Offender and Addiction-Cognitive Behavioral Therapy"
- "The Offender and Addiction-Clinical Case Management"

I also published two books (or technical training manuals).

In 2003, I was named a "Public Health Champion" of the Year, Jefferson County

Department of Health and Environment. In 2008, I received a "Certificate of Accomplishment" for "25 Years of Distinguished Service as a trainer, mentor, and addiction professional," from the Association for Addiction Professionals (NAADAC). And, also in 2008, I was given the "Trainer of the Year Award" by the Alcohol and Drug Programs (ADP) at Safety Center Incorporated (SCI), Sacramento, California. My other awards included "Big Cheese" at Austin-Travis County MHMR, "Service Excellence" at Exempla Lutheran Medical Center, "Extra Mile Club" at Park East Community Mental Health Center, "Gold Star Employee" at St. Luke's Hospital, "Eagle Award" at Centennial Peaks Hospital, "Award for Innovation" at Community Responsibility Center.

RAND KANNENBERG
Crim. Just. Addiction Services

KVIQ-TV (CBS) and KIEM-TV (NBC) labeled me as an "addictions expert" and provided great coverage of my training in Eureka/Fortuna, California. In Denver, KMGH-TV (ABC) interviewed me as an expert again in opposition to the University of Colorado at Denver and Health Sciences Center's Project Safe, a one-year research study "to increase awareness of safer injection." I said that it was unethical to pay human research subjects for using IV Methamphetamine because a single use could result in death.

In 2006, I filed formal complaints regarding unethical advertising against two attorneys from a Denver law firm with the Colorado Supreme Court Attorney Regulation Counsel and was assigned two separate case numbers for their paid ad in a weekly newspaper that read, "The DUI Lawyers" and included this wording, "Memorial Day Tip: Pure alcohol has no odor."

I filed a lawsuit in Denver District Court against John Hickenlooper (then Mayor of Denver). I claimed that he was violating state law (the Clean Indoor Air Act). He was later elected to the office of Colorado Governor. He was also in the Presidential race for a short while this year. Instead, he is running as the 2020 Democrat candidate for a U.S. Senate seat in Colorado. He has been found guilty of ethics charges in the state, the IRS has concluded that he did not pay taxes that were due, and he is being accused of using monies meant for others to pay for his own legal fees. Some also say that he is guilty of accepting donations that were tied to favors.

Needless to say, my professional career was going well, and I still had excessive energy, enthusiasm, and excitement to be involved day and night about social problems around the state. I had no fear of elected officials.

An up?

Chapter Twelve

Family History

As an adult, my younger brother Scott was diagnosed with BD and substance use disorders NOS, but he did not take medications or seek treatment. He was married four times, two times to the same woman. He had issues with physical assault and had other legal problems too. My parents divulged that they spent more than $100,000 on him in his last year of life with legal fees, a new car, and daily expenses. He was accused of using marijuana when one of his children was present.

Scott committed suicide in 2015.

He was in a road rage incident one time where he supposedly assaulted the other driver with a shovel. We aren't sure if he had the shovel and retrieved it from the trunk of his car or if it belonged to the other motorist, but he beat the man across the face and head. Luckily, he survived. Scott went to jail for this assault and later entered an adult halfway house/work release program while I was employed there. That was awkward.

What's really ironic about Scott's illnesses was that he attended an annual meeting with me where I spoke about violence and alcohol-related problems. After one of my first publications, in 1987, I spoke at this conference in Breckenridge, Colorado. Scott traveled with me on the trip and heard me speak, but never seemed to make the connection that he had these same issues at the time. I was talking about him.

When he was in high school, Scott was accused of sexual assault. I do not know if legal action was taken, but I remember our parents and the parents of the girl(s) who made the accusations, along with Scott, met with the principal.

Scott had "groupies" in all small cities where his semi-pro baseball team played. He gave me details of his sexual exploits even though I told him I wasn't interested. He was very graphic.

Many of the women in Scott's life reached out to me and asked for help with the domestic violence. The only suggestion I had was for them to call the police. I still wonder if there's something else I could have done to help.

After one of my attempts, an overdose in the mountains with no one nearby, I was finally discovered and taken by ambulance to the closest hospital. Scott arrived in the ER. He got close to me and whispered, "We have more in common than you know."

As I've said earlier, Scott was physically abusive to our parents. Just the idea that this kind of abuse took place makes me ill. But even with all of his issues, they worshiped him. The prodigal son, that was Scott. Kelly and I could never figure out why Scott was the hero, even after he killed himself.

We have other family members who have also been diagnosed with BD, Substance Use Disorder NOS, depression, anxiety, and Attention Deficit Hyperactivity Disorder (ADHD). Some are like Scott, noncompliant with treatment or medications, and others are coping. These relatives have a range of severity as well and are on one side of my family. To protect their privacy, I won't divulge many more details, but I believe with our strong family history, most of this has to be genetically passed down. As a sociological practitioner, I also believe that many behaviors are learned. There are really two sides to this coin: these traits are genetic, like Type 1 Diabetes (aka "inherited"). My position is that the science is good for both explanations.

As a child and adolescent, I witnessed self-harm: an adult putting his hand and arm through a glass window, and taking small overdoses resulting in many hours of sleep. I learned this. I wasn't born that way.

At five years old, I was sitting in the passenger seat of a car when I heard Kelly screaming. I looked at the backseat and saw that her arm was stuck in a closed window. The driver was arguing with another adult as he was pulling the vehicle out of the garage and didn't notice that Kelly was reaching for that other person outside the car. Kelly does not remember this. She was only three and while the memory is hazy having been so many years ago, I have not forgotten this negligence.

Another time, Scott told Kelly and me that he witnessed a family member putting a pistol in her mouth. I didn't see this firsthand, but I don't think that he would lie about it. These behaviors have stuck with me through the years.

Tricia and I are so thankful that neither of our adult daughters exhibit any indicators of mental illness. They are both extremely successful. I want to respect their privacy, like all other relatives, and will not discuss much more about their personal lives.

Chapter Thirteen

Travels and Parenthood

Ah, adult life. How wonderful it has been to be a parent for 30 years. Tricia and I waited until we had been married for about ten years to have children and we were blessed with two beautiful daughters.

I was a stay-at-home dad for some of my career, and when I was the one primarily home during the day, it wasn't a common thing. Most kids had stay-at-home mothers or caregivers while both parents worked.

One job allowed me to work twelve hour shifts on Friday, Saturday and Sunday for a typical week, which meant I could stay home with the girls Monday through Thursday. My mother would help with them on Fridays. Tricia was no less essential in their upbringing either. We took turns and loved being parents, and still do.

I taught the girls how to ski. Because they learned young, they have no fear of the speed. They were about three years old when they started learning and this was to their advantage.

We had a station wagon and later a van when the girls were growing up. We would travel to National Parks all over the country. We'd make movies on road trips. I had a VHS camcorder and we would shoot many home movies on our travels. To this day, I have saved an old VCR player so we can still watch those old movies. The girls were hilarious and would interview each other at stops along the way. The whole family enjoyed staying at hotels, swimming in the pools and being out on the road. Sometimes we would camp, depending on the destination. We went to both Disneyland and Walt Disney World.

One of our daughters would get terrible carsickness. The other would cry uncontrollably.

She thought her sibling was dying. Thankfully it came in waves and didn't spoil the trips.

I've already said that Tricia and I have been married for forty years. I think back to when my parents were raising us kids and appreciate overall what a sheltered upbringing they provided. I have revealed some exceptions. Tricia and I always tried to do the same, very careful with the girls with regards to what they were exposed to. We would always get background checks for any individuals with the potential to be working with the girls.

We signed our daughters up for preschool and they went a year before kindergarten to get a head start. Tricia and I were both very involved with their schooling. We participated in the PTA, attended all of their recitals, games, and other school and community events. I'm so thankful that our girls have grown very close.

We live on almost a third an acre lot in Lakewood, the same house where the girls grew up.

We didn't want our kids to experience negative things associated with moving like changing schools or changing their circle of friends, so by staying in one place, it provided stability. Sometimes this meant longer commutes to work for me or Tricia, but it was worth the stable environment.

In early 2001, I received a call from the University of Port Elizabeth (or Nelson Mandela University) in the Eastern Cape Province of South Africa, stating that I had been chosen to take a trip there to provide formal training. (The province is famous for violence and shark attacks.) The tickets were pricey, and the university had agreed to pay half and they received a grant from their government to cover the other half of the expenses.

I took a short flight from Denver to the Atlanta airport. While on this two-hour flight, I found out I was on the same plane as the Backstreet Boys and though I'm sure they were annoyed by my asking, they graciously signed something as a souvenir to take back to our daughters.

My next flight was just as memorable but for different reasons. The nearly 18-hour nonstop flight from Atlanta to the Republic of South Africa (RSA) was exhausting. The jet lag was horrible upon arrival and it took a bit for me to adjust. At 17 hours and 45 minutes to be exact, it was referred to as "the longest flight in the world." And it most certainly seemed that way.

Despite my sleep struggles, the trip was worth it all.

While there, I saw 22 elephants in the wild, including a mother who became aggressive because of her young calf. We were way too close to the elephants, but as a tourist, I wanted to see and get pictures. You weren't supposed to get out of your vehicle on these viewing safaris, but my friend from the RSA said it would be okay. I had a disposable camera and wanted a good shot. Mama elephant's ears perked up and I snapped my photo and quickly got back in the vehicle.

I really missed Tricia, specifically while I was away on this trip. Back then we had calling cards and I'd call her from a pay phone, punching in the long string of numbers from the card. Just like reporters on television who are far away, there was a big delay in our words as they traveled halfway around the world to the other end of the line. I got really emotional when I called her, and she couldn't hear me. It was good to get home when the trip ended.

I received a call from my university contact that my host at the bed and breakfast in the RSA who had also become a friend, was shot and killed by a 16-year-old a week after I left. The teen wanted his cash and apparently, he wouldn't give it up easily. And this was post-Apartheid.

An RSA official sent me a huge bouquet of flowers after 9/11. I thought this was a kind gesture.

My trips later in life with Tricia and the girls are also great memories for me. We went to Alaska and Hawaii together and took our daughters to London, Paris and Rome. Schooling was very important in our family and this was the first time we took the girls out of school. The principal immediately agreed to the trip as she said they'd get to learn firsthand the cultures that are out there to soak up.

I mentioned I saw the Backstreet Boys on a previous trip, I also had run-ins with Cameron Diaz, Jessica Simpson and Donald Sutherland while traveling.

I really enjoyed trips to Indian reservations, specifically the Eastern Band of Cherokee Indians in Cherokee, North Carolina; Miccosukee Tribe of Indians in Miami, Florida; and Sisseton Wahpeton Oyate of the Lake Traverse Reservation, (formerly Sisseton-Wahpeton Sioux Tribe/Dakota Nation). I remember how people would come into talks and roundtables a couple of minutes up to a half-hour late. They would all say, it was okay, "you're on Indian time."

Another favorite trip was where I presented at Convegno Internazionale di Sociologia Clinica, Salerno, Italy. I'll let you figure out what that means because I still don't know.

In addition to working in all fifty states, I've traveled to places outside the United States, and am fascinated with seeing the world and all the different cultures.

Chapter Fourteen

Physical Assaults as an Adult

In 1982, Tricia and I were both employed at the same residential childcare facility (RCCF) in Lakewood. RCCFs were a place for youth who were "emotionally disturbed," "intellectually disabled" and "severely autistic" (common diagnoses at the time) to live in a private residence. One evening, the director/homeowner asked me to retrieve the older kids from the basement because it was time for dinner. When I got to the last step, I saw that all of the lights were turned off. One adolescent was hiding from staff in the dark. What felt like slow motion but was over in an instant, and that was a big and very strong 17-year-old with a history of violence, hitting me with all his might in the face and mouth. I heard the noise before I could feel the pain and taste the blood. Hindsight, he didn't know who I was, and I hadn't said anything as I descended the stairs. Mistakes were made on both parts that night.

A trip to the hospital and x-rays showed I had a fractured alveolar process (the bony ridge that holds the teeth). I required several oral and maxillofacial surgeries to recover. It affected my chewing.

I avoided all of the male adolescents after this happened, and an alarm in my mind sounded when they got too close. The RCCF did not have worker's compensation insurance, which resulted in the owners having to pay me double my current and future medical bills. They blamed me for getting them in trouble with the Colorado Department of Labor and Employment. Tricia and I continued to work there until corporal punishment with objects like wooden spoons were used on the residents.

This assault caused disturbing dreams and flashbacks about the incident. I told my PCP about this and requested a referral to the mental health department at the same insurance company. I had a single appointment and did not return because the Ph.D. psychologist was inappropriate. Actually, he was nuts. He told me that if he was having a difficult time enjoying sex with his wife, he would fantasize about raping another woman he was attracted to.

I was the patient.

And I was there to talk about how to avoid a lifetime with PTSD.

I should have complained, but I was young, still in school and ignorant as to airing a grievance in this type of matter. I was not yet certified or licensed myself. To this day, I regret not coming forward and reporting him. I sincerely hope he didn't cause ill thoughts or harm to other patients after me.

Thanksgiving weekend in 1993, I was working as the clinical care coordinator for four locked inpatient psychiatric units. An elderly patient fell out of his bed four times and was found dead on the floor after his fourth fall. This was the first death on any of our psychiatric units. It was also the first time that I, and most of my peers, saw a dead body in person.

The next day, in the same unit, a patient fashioned a weapon out of a large aluminum pop can and threatened a mental health worker. I witnessed this incident. Today, mental health patients in most if not all facilities are only given small cans that cannot be twisted and torn.

On day three of this series of traumatic events, a female patient was let out of restraints by a medical/surgical LPN who was filling in for other staff because of the holiday weekend. He was obviously not trained in mental health. He thought it was cruel to have this patient in some restraints, making it hard to eat. She escaped from the room when he took her out of restraints, further escaping from the unit when someone was entering (these days units have double doors making such escapes much less possible), took a housekeeper hostage, repeatedly assaulted me, resulting in three surgeries to repair my inguinal wall and genitofemoral nerve. Her husband got off of the elevator for a multifamily support group that I facilitated with a female nurse and female social worker. He began to hit and kick the staff. He didn't understand why this was happening to his naked wife. We were attempting to safely carry her back to the unit and seclusion room, but she broke away from the staff on the floor and the hospital security officer held her from behind.

I saw the patient repeatedly elbowing him in the chest with both arms. Shortly after all of this was resolved and I made certain that the nurses and techs received medical care in the ER, two young girls visiting at the hospital were screaming and telling me that a man was hurt and where he was located. The man in trouble was Dwight, the same security officer that saved the day on the unit. After assessing him I told the girls to please go to the ER and tell them what was going on. I started CPR. It was terrible! I could hear the sound of his ribs breaking after doing some chest compressions. No one from the American Red Cross told me to expect that when performing CPR. In just a few minutes a crash cart with emergency workers arrived and took over for me. He was declared dead shortly after that. The blows to his chest were fatal. The hospital told us not to talk about it and said he died because of a history of heart disease which, according to them, is why he retired on a disability from the Denver Police Department.

I later suggested that there be a phone added to the common area between the four units where we worked so someone could call for help in case of another emergency like this in the future. The hospital did not fulfill this request. During a meeting with hospital attorneys, we were warned not to go to Dwight's funeral or call the family.

I also thought it was appropriate to send flowers and a sympathy card to the family of the patient who died after falling out of bed four times. The nurse manager got very angry with me saying the gesture was admitting guilt on the hospital's part. I did not ask for reimbursement.

At my request, I was later referred by human resources to an employee assistance program where an inexperienced therapist cried as I was telling my story. I felt horrible. I thought I had caused her harm. It didn't help me with my problems. It only made them worse. Eventually, I saw a psychiatrist who specialized in what he called "battle fatigue." Before I saw him, to fall asleep I was drinking two shots of whiskey before I went to bed for three or so months. In order for alcohol consumption to be considered problematic, it must be abused for 12 consecutive months. After one year, a diagnosis can be made. I knew I was on track for this to become a problem, which was a good time to stop. I have not had alcohol since 1993.

In 2010, at a well-known detoxification facility in the Denver area (that is now closed), I was assaulted by a male patient who I approached because I witnessed him using street drugs in the program. The hard strike by him to my right arm bruised the bone, requiring physical therapy. The worst part of this incident was when the local police department came and arrested him for assault, he told me with others within hearing distance that the next time he saw me, he would kill me. A District Court judge granted me a permanent restraining order against him, but the agency that employed me said that they would not abide by the judge's order "because it (was) not good for business," even when I suggested that the patient could be transported to one of the other locations owned by the same agency.

I immediately resigned and made my first near-fatal suicide attempt that day because I wanted to have more say in my own death and knew I could no longer tolerate physical injuries to me from others who I was trying to help.

Chapter Fifteen

Laughter was the Best Medicine

Before the girls were born, Tricia and I had a little side business selling bumper stickers. I made the design which incorporated both the American and Colorado flags and had them professionally printed at a local print shop. We would go to the Denver Broncos games and sell them for $1.25 to make a little money.

We would enjoy talking to the fans who were tailgating in the different stadium parking lots. Some of them gave very positive feedback, saying that they had never seen a bumper sticker like what we had. It was always nice seeing so many smiling faces. We laughed.

Many of the adults were getting close to being intoxicated after drinking hours before the game started.

I give my dad credit for this endeavor as he was a great role model for being self-employed.

***

After the series of events at the hospital, I took a break from working directly in the mental health field and decided to "treat" people with laughter. I opened a standup comedy club named "Comedy Clinic: A good laugh is great therapy" because I love to see people laugh and I needed to do something different.

My favorite local comedy club had no admission charge but had an expensive minimum drink order and the whole place was full of second-hand smoke. I could not believe how people sat in the smoke-filled room, barely able to see through the grey clouds to watch the performers.

I charged a small admission fee (I believe it was $7.50) and did not have a minimum drink requirement. I had three-two beer, which could be consumed at 18 years old, and a self-serve snack bar. In the afternoons, I would even take the girls to help me setup. They enjoyed partaking in the caramel corn and other snacks. It was unlike any setup of a comedy club I had ever been to. In Boulder, home to the flagship campus of the University of Colorado, I aimed to please the potential audience.

I hired great comedians and paid them well. I would have an emcee, the middle act, and the headliner. They told me behind closed doors it was a nice place. Onstage they made fun that the club was so small. I applied for and received a maximum occupancy of 100 for the space.

I learned firsthand that many comedians were funny on stage but didn't have the best lives when they weren't performing. They put all of their happiness and laughter into their jobs. In my opinion, many of them had mood disorders. Sounded like me.

I had a sold-out show for New Year's Eve. Everyone was given sparkling cider and noisemakers.

The club lasted for about nine months and many others closed the same year. Large networks like HBO and Showtime started playing more comedy shows in their late-night lineups. It was cheaper and easier for people to stay home and watch TV regularly than going out to a club.

This was my chance to try to do something different than psychiatry and chemical dependency. When the club shutdown, I went back to the same hospital where the traumas occurred as a clinical care coordinator.

BD can cause issues with impulse control and I can admit that I didn't have good impulse control when it came to my employment. Throughout my career, if I saw something better, I'd jump at the opportunity, oftentimes without thinking it through before taking the leap.

Ups and downs.

Ups and downs.

Chapter Sixteen

Using Painting as Therapy

In college, I started painting as a way to relax and take my mind off of things. I used oil paint and made one piece on canvas for an art class.

The first thing I painted was a picture of the father, son and holy ghost and received an A for a grade. I gave it to my cousin and her husband, a minister, as a wedding gift. They both loved it.

While I was in the hospital for genitofemoral nerve surgery, I was able to paint, because I could keep still. Tricia brought paints, brushes and a canvas to the hospital so I had something to look forward to while I was healing.

My paintings are abstract art, and varied colors from one to the next. I always liked adding black to bright colors. People always tell me I should have saved more of my paintings. But I enjoy donating them to therapists and programs where they will be seen, rather than leaving them sitting in a corner to later be sold in a garage sale.

I never saw myself as having a talent for painting, I had always enjoyed seeing what I could come up with.

Chapter Seventeen

Furry Friends

Later in life, after we had lost our beloved MacKenzie and pets since her, I decided to get a dog to act as a companion and support animal. In 2013, I found a Newfoundland Labrador crossbreed, or a Newfie-Lab for short. He was definitely still a puppy, approximately 2 months old at the time. I called Tricia as I was driving to Boulder from the therapist's office in the Denver area who I had just told. I don't remember how Tricia reacted, but she later told me she didn't have a say in the matter. Her concern was that a puppy was a big responsibility we were suddenly taking on. I was also very ill at the time.

We named him Joey.

In the beginning, I was interested in Joey becoming a service dog, but the cost for training back then was upwards of $15,000. I found online courses where I could self-teach Joey, but I was too sick to do it myself. Unfortunately, Joey had some behavior problems and he did not work well as a companion/support animal.

If I was crying, sometimes Joey would come to comfort me by resting his head on my chest. Sometimes he would put his face in my face to remind me everything was going to be okay. He was a great friend to me.

We would take Joey on trips with us. He had a vest with an identification badge that said he was a working dog.

Joey died when he was seven years old. I found him stiff in his crate when I woke that morning.

I appreciated the person who came out to take him to the cremation services for pets. He was very nice and professional, and they returned the ashes in a nice container with a certificate of death. I received a very caring call from the tech at the veterinarian's office and a sympathy card from the veterinarian.

The sadness of Joey's passing brought back many memories from the events I witnessed while working at the hospital many years before. It doesn't make sense to some people, but this loss reminded me of Dwight's death. Once again, I felt hopeless. I couldn't do anything to bring Joey back.

We waited a while, but not too long to get another dog, Daisy, an American Akita.

My doctor and therapist both said that Daisy and I are a match, as we both have been abused in the past. While we don't know what happened to Daisy, she would exhibit behavior such as lip curling and growling. In the beginning, she would bark and come very close to biting me.

Daisy was found online during the early times in the COVID-19 pandemic. All of the shelters near us were closed except in the cases where they had to deal with foster families. The listing led us to contact the owners for more information. They said she had all of her vaccinations and promised to send us medical records to review, but never did. We finally gave up asking for those. Our vet said it would be safer to have her vaccinations a second time rather than risk her not having them at all.

Tricia really wanted a pet this time and Daisy came very attached to her. She didn't ride in a car well or walk with a leash easily.

Prior to her adoption (and sometime after) I received negative feedback from family, and my psychiatrist who brought up that Akitas had a reputation of being extremely aggressive. Akitas are typically trained to hunt larger animals like bears and while I no longer hunted and had no desire to raise Daisy as a hunting dog, her instincts provided a concern.

My doctor admitted to me that she also has an Akita. It is not common for psychiatrists (at least mine) to share things about their personal lives with their patients. I was most definitely paying attention when we talked about this as I appreciated the reciprocal sharing.

Except for her not liking me at first (thankfully she's gotten over that), Daisy has had no real behavioral issues. I take her on walks. Though she's still afraid of cars, she does better when they approach. Her actions indicate she has had some trauma with vehicles in her past. Some kind of memory is there for her. She does well with other people and they often comment on how beautiful she is. Daisy is very well behaved. As Tricia and I age, we acknowledge that Daisy will likely be our last dog.

I myself am not a cat person.

Tricia, however, is.

We have two cats, named Louie and Pumpkin. Pumpkin is most definitely Tricia's cat. Louie is mine.

I often find myself getting irritated with the cats. Pumpkin meows all the time. It's hard for me to concentrate with his incessant noisemaking.

When we got the cats, we had to sign documents agreeing that they could not be outdoor cats, only on occasion with a collar, leash or harness, and they could not be declawed. They damage furniture and their cat toys with their claws, and this also annoys me. We clip their nails as needed.

Tricia really loves cats, so when it was time to get Pumpkin, the girls helped me deceive and surprise Tricia. I drove from Denver to Fort Collins to adopt Pumpkin because Tricia had always wanted another orange tabby mix. I went to pick her up and came home to surprise Tricia. She was pleased with our new addition.

Chapter Eighteen

Suicide Attempts and Admissions

In 2010, after the third incident of being seriously assaulted by a patient who said that he would kill me the next time we were together, I was not in a good place. My thoughts were if my employer at the time couldn't ensure my safety and was just going to let the patient who said he would kill me come into my place of work and harm me, I wanted some control over my own death. That control turned into a suicide attempt.

My birthday was the day I wrote the resignation letter and decided to take that control into my own hands. I was so focused on the task that I even dated the letter with my actual birthday, February 28, 1960, instead of 2010. I had just received new prescriptions for the medicines I regularly took (Saphris, Klonopin and Ambien) and to cheat the system or be tricky, I went to a drug store that I did not regularly use for prescriptions and told them I had no insurance and planned to pay cash. On bated breath I waited for those prescriptions to be filled. I bought a couple one-fifth bottles of rum, the largest I could find, and went to a hotel far away from our home to consume my fate.

I hadn't had a drink since 1993 when I started drinking to sleep better. And at this point in my life, I wasn't drinking to get drunk or to start a new habit. I was putting a means to an end.

This event ruined all future birthdays because the attempt at taking my own life will forever be associated.

I was in a coma and intubated (on a ventilator) for a short period of time. I remember at one point hearing the doctor say that I was "not out of the woods yet." Eighteen hours after the last drink, my blood alcohol level was still .591, which is extremely high. In all of the U.S., a blood alcohol level of 0.08 is "intoxicated" making it unlawful for the person to operate a motor vehicle. And a level above 0.40 is potentially fatal. Because of this, the suicide attempt came very close to being successful.

Later that year, I made another attempt.

I consumed a full bottle of Tylenol Extra Strength, 100 tablets, 500 mg. each. I told Tricia in time and a friend drove both of us to the emergency room. The physician called the local poison control and they instructed the ER staff to give me a medication called Mucomyst. I had to take so many doses until the Tylenol level in my blood was normal again. This type of treatment is usually effective up to four hours after consumption and I remember letting Tricia know what I had done two hours after I took the pills.

In the field that I worked, I knew Tylenol was dangerous. When evaluating patients, I had observed some taking Tylenol in extremely large quantities. I knew the aftereffects could potentially cause major organ damage.

For the next ten years, I was admitted to the hospital ten times for depression and/or mania. These admissions over the years included several "M-1 Holds." As you can imagine, I already knew from my career what these holds were and how they worked. A mental health hold can be used when a patient is deemed to be in imminent danger of harming him or herself or someone else, or unable to care for basic daily needs. These holds rely on the Colorado Revised Statute 27-65-101 Care and Treatment of Persons with Mental Illness. When a person is placed on a mental health hold, it means that they can be held for up to 72 hours for a psychiatric evaluation. Overdoses from prescription medications resulted in several M-1 Holds for me during this decade of my life. Additional psychiatric admissions were for confusion or psychosis.

These events would admit me to two different hospitals near me and one of which provided stellar patient care. The other facility provided poor care and I had many issues there. Yet a third hospital administered my bedtime medications that caused sedation in the morning. It took Tricia a long time advocating on my behalf that this was an error and they needed to check with my physician to have it changed.

There is one incident in particular that sticks out in my mind. I'm convinced that it really happened. Tricia thinks I was delusional. Whether that was the case or not, I have a vivid memory of three nurses getting irritated with me because I had fallen three times during their shift. They badgered me asking why I kept falling, did I slip because the surface was wet or my socks were slick, did I trip on something, etc., and finally took me to another unit where I was more controlled. I explained to them they weren't responding to me very well and it was not my fault I kept falling. The only injury was a bruise on my knee.

I was on an M-1 Hold at the time and when that happens, the patient has certain rights, which of course I knew. I was denied paper and pencils, envelopes and stamps and they refused to let me use the phone. I wanted to talk to another doctor and was denied the ability.

Other admissions to day-treatment programs (partial hospitalization programs) took place over the years. When my psychiatrist was running out of ideas, we opted for a different kind of treatment-a twenty-eight day stay in a residential program in Florida. Since I was a Certified Case Manager, I was able to get myself admitted to this program without anyone helping.

I called several dozen programs to see if I could get admitted and they were either full or not in-network with our insurance company. My psychiatrist at the time said enough was enough and I needed to go to a residential program. I wanted one closer to home, because residents in the program that had families nearby were able to visit with them. I didn't have that luxury and it was a long month away from Tricia and the girls.

I flew by myself from Denver to Clearwater, Florida. There were a few different kinds of addictions in the Florida facility. People had eating disorders, substance abuse or dependence, or sex addiction. While there for almost a month, I overheard a lot of the residents having sex on a regular basis. I was actually able to hear it through the walls. This was against the program rules. I had a male roommate, but the sexes were not separated by wings, only rooms.

They had a variety of groups, meetings and activities. Most of the patients had a substance use disorder and a mental health disorder. We earned passes based on good behavior and I used these to leave the facility and go to the beach. The campus was several miles away from the beautiful white sand beaches in Clearwater, but I wanted to go. So I walked to the Island from the facility to see and play in the ocean.

The Church of Scientology has a base in Clearwater. They had men in suits and ties walking the perimeter of the campus building and parking lots.

I made two friends in Clearwater. My roommate and I have fallen out of contact over the last couple years. And I really liked a female resident. I developed a bit of a childhood crush on her. We were both happily married of course, and nothing happened.

The Florida program was good, I gave it great reviews. While my time there was good, I was ready to get home.

Another time my psychiatrist wanted to explore electroconvulsive therapy (ECT), which most people don't even think is still being done in this day and age, but we went there. Most imagine it to look like something out of the movie *One Flew*

Over the Cuckoo's Nest, but it has become much more sophisticated. It was like having a dozen surgical procedures being done. I had to have anti-anxiety medication ahead of time so I could be calm. Once I was still and ready, they administered a general anesthesia. They gave me electric currents through my brain to trigger a seizure. The doctors said I had "good seizures," whatever that meant. Over the course of 12 sessions, I experienced profound short-term memory loss. I still have issues remembering things that happened during the timeframe I was receiving the ECT. Thankfully, I had no long-term memory loss.

The U.S. Food and Drug Administration (FDA) approved ECT for bipolar in 2018. So I was having this done years prior to this approval. I had to stop taking both anticonvulsant medications so I could have seizures. ECT has had a good success rate with people who are depressed. I received all 12 sessions, three times a week for one month. Tricia and my parents took turns driving me. The ECT was done at the same hospital where Tricia worked at the time (she was there for twenty years).

Unrelated, I have about a one year span about which I have very few memories. Two possible explanations are catatonia (like schizophrenia), according to Tricia, a speech language pathologist who also does cognitive evaluations like psychologists, and dissociation (a mild form of multiple personality disorder) per my psychologist.

I took the Montreal Cognitive Assessment (MoCA) more than a year ago because of problems with my memory.

The highest possible score is 30. Normal is 26 and above. My first score was 14. I failed. My second score about 6 months later was 22, a good increase but still not normal.

The third time I took the test my result was 28. I missed 2 items requiring me to draw pictures. My hand tremors and anxiety both interfered with my performance. Again, I was the patient.

This is after many years of me, the therapist, administering the other evaluation commonly used, the Mini Mental Status Exam (MMSE) during psychiatric assessments in the emergency departments where I worked.

I was suicidal around five years ago. I officially owned the rifle that I had used to hunt the deer more than 40 years earlier. I was scared to death. Isn't it ironic that those are the best words I can think of? But I immediately wanted to get rid of the gun and the bullets. I was in a dangerous way because of a "mixed mood," depression with suicidal ideation, and mania with enough energy to get the job done.

I drove to my therapist's office because it was only a mile or two away. I knocked on her door to find she was with another patient. Very quickly I told her what was in my car. She walked outside to the parking lot with me and took the rifle and ammunition and put them in her trunk.

Tricia was called and she left work early to pick me up. A close family friend with no known mental health problems agreed to take everything from Tricia and I have never been happier to have that gun out of my life.

In early 2020, I went to a gun store to purchase a pistol with the intent to take my own life. I didn't just go out and purchase a gun. My plan was to shoot myself in my heart, mainly because I wanted to be able to have an open-casket funeral service.

I handed the cashier my credit card, which he swiped and gave back to me with the receipt. As the manager was putting the pistol in its box, two Lakewood police cars pulled up to the shop. The store was notified by a "BOLO" (be on the lookout for) from the Colorado Bureau of Investigations. They told the store that I was ineligible to purchase a gun. This happened because Tricia called 911.

My daughter and son-in-law were at our house, which was not far from the gun shop, and they quickly drove up to the store. It broke my heart for my daughter to see me handcuffed and placed into the back of a squad car.

Weeks later, my family, supported by my doctor, petitioned the court for an Extreme Risk Protection Order (ERPO). I was one of the first persons in Colorado to receive an ERPO and was the very first in Jefferson County. Other city and county attorneys attended the hearing because it was one of the first times this had happened in our state. Also known as the "Red Flag Law," it had just been approved in Colorado and my family wanted to ensure I no longer had access to weapons. This of course made me worried about my reputation.

Three police officers wore bullet-proof vests when delivering the notice to appear to my house to inform me of the ERPO. I should have known working with patients that domestic issues were often the most dangerous for police and they were only protecting themselves from the scene they were walking into. They were joined by a Licensed Clinical Social Worker from the local mental health center.

The results from the hearing were my inability to possess a handgun for one year. I eventually realized my family members did this because they love and care about me. I told my court-appointed attorney in February 2020 that I did not want to fight my family's petition for an ERPO. However, I will contest any attempt to renew it for another year, which is an option under the legislation, because I have had no suicidal ideation using a gun or any other means since that time.

I had terrible periods of time where I felt extreme hopelessness and found suicide was the only option available for relief. People say that suicide is a very selfish thing to do. Some would even have the audacity to ask me if I thought about my family members and what I would be leaving behind. But what was not understood by others looking into my situation is that I felt like I was making my family members as unhappy as I was inside. At surface level, like my comedians?

I wasn't able to be a loving husband and a good father. I wasn't able to be a good friend. If I couldn't take care of my own situation, how was I to be able to care for my loved ones?

My attempts were lethal with no opportunity to escape without immediate assistance that Tricia was able to provide. My last attempt would have had no recourse if I had made it outside of the gun shop that cold winter day.

Chapter Nineteen

Migraines: A Pain in the...Head

Since I was barely an adult, I've dealt with migraines. At the age of 18, I was diagnosed with migraines and at the time prescribed an opioid called Darvocet. This drug has since been removed from the market for increased risk for a variety of serious medical complications. While I was taking Darvocet and having frequent, recurring migraines, I was unable to operate a motor vehicle. Most of the time Tricia would drive as I was dealing with blurred vision and nausea. There were times I'd have to ask her to pull the car over so I could vomit. This went on for about four years. Thankfully at age 22, the frequency of recurrence slowed down.

The migraines came back with a vengeance two other times in my life, when I was in my thirties and again in my fifties. When not in these heavy times, I've always still had them, just not quite as often. I also get severe headaches when exposed to temperature changes (from cold to hot), and loud noises with vibration (neighbor's car stereo) and am very sensitive to bright lights. I also experience "post coital migraines," not something that's easy to talk about with my female neurologist.

I still limit my driving when I have a migraine or strong headache that may turn worse for the same reasons. The last thing I want to do is cause an accident because my vision is blurry, or I get nauseous. On a regular day, our girls still do not think it is a good idea for me to drive and will not ride as a passenger in my car if I am driving.

I currently take a triptan medication as needed at the onset of a migraine and the antidepressant I take daily helps deal with migraines in addition to mood and sleep as well. I have to take an additional medication to decrease both nausea and vomiting which are side effects. I try this medicine first because it is for pain and nausea and then if that doesn't knock it, I take the triptan to try and drive it home.

At home, I respond really well to three things that have nothing to do with medication. I have very good results with ice, turning the lights off in our bedroom and experiencing the white noise of our box fan.

As an additional form of treatment, I receive Botox injections every 12 weeks. The FDA has approved Botox for people who experience 15 or more headaches a month and I easily fall into that category. Having side effects from Botox are not very common, but then I am an overachiever and experience being tired one to two days after the injections. How ironic is it that the Botox which can be used for migraines, often causes me and others to have a headache?

The procedure consists of 31 injections each visit, five units per injection for a total of 155 units. I receive these injections at the back of my head, my forehead, both temples, shoulders and back. The needles are pretty small and not too painful.

I keep a daily log of my headaches for the doctor, using a rating scale from one to ten with one being little to no headache, to ten being bad enough to go to the emergency room for IV medications. I do not track migraines that I consider to be a six or lower, only with an intensity of seven, eight or nine. Seven is an average number for me and I experience this intensity of a migraine on average three to four times a week. I also chart nausea and vomiting to make sure there aren't any issues with my medication.

My neurologist has diagnosed me with debilitating migraines as I am unable to function when they come on. At the onset of a migraine, I know my next few hours to days will be spent at home, doing all the remedies that have proven to help me and taking my additional medications as needed. These specific medications cause drowsiness and I am unable to operate motor vehicles or heavy machinery, but that was probably obvious. As a result of taking these medicines, I have both bone and joint pain and weakness. It feels like a really bad case of the flu and I ache all over.

I recently had a CT scan of my head to rule out any other causes for the pain and the radiologist discovered that I had a stroke about two years ago (she diagnosed this on the basis of my last CT scan a couple of years ago being normal). I had no symptoms and never knew it had occurred. Where Tricia is an expert at looking for strokes and working with patients who have had a stroke, we found it strange she had never noticed anything with me either. It was likely a mini-stroke or a transient ischemic attack (TIA), but I'm not doing anything or taking any medications to decrease the likelihood of having it reoccur.

Chapter Twenty

The Ups and Downs, Day to Day

Currently, I exhibit the following symptoms when ill (relapsed): Post Traumatic Stress Disorder (PTSD), Generalized Anxiety Disorder (GAD), Obsessive-Compulsive Disorder (OCD) and Bipolar I Disorder.

PTSD causes me to have both nightmares and flashbacks. I avoid stressors similar to the original events and experience what's called hypervigilance. This means that I am very alert. Accordingly, I have an immediate startle response. I believe that PTSD can trigger the onset of BD. Those traumatic events in 1982, 1993 and 2010 contribute to this illness.

For a while, my PCP of 33 years thought that my PTSD was the primary diagnosis and that I needed eye movement desensitization and reprocessing treatment (EMDR). My psychologist disagreed saying that I was bipolar, first. Common literature these days says that PTSD can precipitate bipolar. You have traumatic events and because a patient is predisposed to having BD because of a family history, PTSD can cause bipolar to happen sooner.

I have an overwhelming fear of going crazy or dying due to anxiety (GAD). I am lightheaded, feel dizzy, and have difficulty breathing. Panic attacks are a real and regularly occurring symptom.

OCD is not often what the general public thinks. I don't just "count things" or "check things." I have an irrational fear of contamination. And, I constantly clean (myself and the house). I take several showers a day. Sometimes I wash until I bleed. I check to see if I definitely locked the doors, over and over. I check my wallet to see if all of my credit cards, cash, and blank checks are accounted for. In extreme situations, I drive around the block a second time to make certain that I didn't hit a person or an animal. In my daily showers discussed above,

I also count that I washed each body part an exact number of times.

Major depressive episodes can be attributed to Bipolar I Disorder. I experience sadness, tearfulness, crying, feelings of hopelessness/helplessness, thoughts of death, and more, regularly. I also have episodes of mania including scenarios of elevated mood, increased energy/excitement/enthusiasm, decreased need for sleep, hypersexuality, and over spending. For me specifically, impulsive behavior examples include situations where I've called a real estate agent about a home appraisal without consulting Tricia, bought and sold cars on my own, and getting tattoos and piercings.

The mood swings I have are both with or without psychosis (they may be visual/auditory hallucinations and/or paranoid delusions and more). When I'm not doing well, it is common for me to have problems with televisions. I get confused about what's being said or shown, mostly during commercials. Some of my psychotic clients in the past thought that their TVs were talking to them. That's not the case with me.

During the recurrence of episodes, I am also very much bothered by the sound of toilets flushing.

In 1980, the name of the BD diagnosis was changed by the American Psychiatric Association (APA) in the third revised edition of the Diagnostic and Statistical Manual (DSM-III-R) because the medical community was convinced that manic was confused with the word "maniac." The APA is currently using the DSM-V.

When the COVID-19 pandemic occurred, I was already washing my hands like a surgeon. This was nothing new for me. But the concerns of social distancing and the spread of germs haven't been far from my mind.

The stress of the Black Lives Matter movement also causes anxiety. I worry about people, in general, and do not accept people being treated unfairly.

Currently, I meet with my psychiatrist every three months, my psychologist every other week, and my social support group every week. My sessions with my psychiatrist are focused on medication management, examining the strength, dosage and frequency of each drug. During my twice-a-month appointments with my psychologist, we focus on mindfulness and self-help techniques.

In my weekly social support group, the facilitator is a certified therapeutic recreation specialist (CTRS). She has games, social activities like holiday and birthday parties, and other activities that are held outdoors including walks. As far as I know, I am one of two persons in the group who have BD and I often have to remind myself that I am not in charge of the group. Again, I was certified with a specialty in small group therapy, so getting out of my own head is often hard.

Sociologists are few and far between these days. I'm forever indebted to my uncle who really opened up the mental health field to me and helped me make the right connections. I have to remember to let all of my providers do their jobs and not take over.

My day-to-day consists of at-home responsibilities and occasionally meeting friends for coffee. I have twelve well-defined friends whom I meet on average once a month. Some are former schoolmates, former coworkers, a former employer and supervisor. Most of my coworkers didn't know I was mentally ill when we worked together. I did a good job of self-regulating and I got along with almost everybody.

In my thirty-year career, I had increasingly responsible positions from entry-level therapist to acting team leader, supervisor, manager, director, and eventually owned my own company. I'm grateful to the friends I made over the years who have stuck by my side.

I regularly meet with a former professor who is now just a good friend.

Remember Todd C.? We still talk on the phone or text and get coffee once in a while.

On a daily basis, I currently take many medications. I am allergic to Lithium and Effexor. I had anaphylaxis with both, swelling and funny sensations of my lips and tongue. When admitted to an inpatient unit, I am given an armband listing the allergic reactions.

I also avoid Pseudoephedrine like the plague. When I was still working, in some circles I was called "Mr. Meth" because my topic on how to treat Methamphetamine dependents was a favorite nation-wide. Pseudoephedrine is an ingredient of Meth. It's only sold behind the counter now. And for me personally, it causes mania, with or without psychosis.

For bipolar and psychosis, I have been prescribed 600 mg. of an atypical, new generation antipsychotic, which I take daily. Another friend of mine also takes the same medication, but she only takes 25 mg and this smaller dose knocks her out. For me, it also causes some sedation and abnormal involuntary movements, such as tremors (I can't shave my head or wear contacts anymore), lip-smacking, and an increase in my weight, blood sugar and cholesterol.

I also take an anti-anxiety medication that is not a benzodiazepine. This is for stress and has a side effect of sedation, which can be a good or bad thing depending on the patient. I benefit from the positives of this medication.

I have been prescribed an antidepressant. My personal adverse reaction is dry mouth. It's a tricyclic withdrawn from the market by the FDA from the market in 2000 because of potential cardiac problems. It is still used for some patients in extreme cases, like me.

I take two different anti-seizure medications also known as anticonvulsants – I take them for bipolar, I don't have a history of seizures. I have no negative side effects or adverse reactions to these medications.

And a long list of vitamins, supplements and minerals that are known to help with mental illness. Sexual performance problems are a common negative side effect with many of my psychiatric medications.

With the severity of GAD, PTSD and OCD in addition to BD, there are things I try to keep at the forefront of my thoughts. One goal I have is to prevent me from falling far down to the ground when depressed.

{DOWN}

Another goal is to prevent me from bouncing high to the ceiling when manic.

{UP}

A third objective is to prevent severe mood swings by maintaining myself and walking steadily on the wire. This is achieved by balancing my mental health with both medications and psychotherapy.

The metaphor of walking the tightrope is a real and everyday occurrence.

So what does my day-to-day look like functioning with BD? Tricia and I sit down once a week, typically on Saturday mornings, to set out my medications for the following week. I have a 7-day medicine dispenser with slots marked morning, noon, evening and bedtime. I have four alarms on my phone that coincide with when I need to take my medications, so I do not forget or get off schedule.

Due to my suicide attempts, my medicines are all stored in a safe that Tricia keeps for me.

Even with all the medicines I take, I'm still able to drive a car. I have learned that I have to slow down and not tailgate. Last year, I was responsible for an accident because of my medications. It caused extreme drowsiness and I was not prepared. I ran a red light and the other car that I struck had entered the intersection too early. There were cameras, which helped our insurance company. They settled the case and it was deemed 70 percent my fault and 30 percent the fault of the other driver for being in the intersection. She also admitted to using marijuana earlier that day. Once my medicines were regulated, I haven't had the extreme drowsiness and am able to drive normally.

I do chores around the house like washing dishes after breakfast, lunch and dinner daily. I take out the trash and recycling containers once a week. I make the bed every morning, vacuum the living room, clean all three of our bathrooms, sweep in the kitchen and dining room and clean up after the dog. I also feed Daisy three times a day, which is quite the task as she has vitamins and additives that have to be prepared in dry and canned food. Staying busy helps me feel responsible.

Sadly, when I'm really sick and relapsing, I can't even do the simplest chores. I had a personal goal of being both depression and manic free for as long as two years and I didn't even come close to reaching it. The symptoms of having a recurrence of bipolar can happen at any time, even when I'm totally compliant with my medications and therapy appointments and be sure to get a good night's rest, relapses can occur. When I am depressed, I tend to have an increased need for sleep, and just the opposite when I have manic episodes, I have a decreased need for sleep.

Regularly, Tricia goes to the grocery store on Saturday mornings. She also is better than me about walking...she tries to drag me out of the house, and I will admit that I don't always go. When the wildfires cause poor air quality, it makes it hard for me because of my asthma to be outside for long periods of time.

I go to the community center for adults 50 years of age and older three times a week. I have lunch there and visit with friends. Tricia tells me to "watch out for those widows." They really have flirted with me!

I also go to the city's recreation center three days a week to work out.

We also have a strict schedule with Friday nights being our date night. We go to dinner, order in or get takeout, just the two of us. It's one routine we both look forward to every week. We like to try new places and new things. We also go out with other couples on Saturday nights once in a while, I enjoy seeing our friends. For us, dinner is usually around 5 p.m. and most people think it's bizarre we eat so early.

In addition to our Friday night dinner dates, we would go to the movies until I could no longer sit still. I started having panic attacks in the theatre after the movie had been playing a while. I'd have to go out and stand in the lobby to calm down. Once that became a regular occurrence, we nixed movie dates.

Tricia is a fantastic cook. She learned from her mother (who was diagnosed with cancer and wanted to prepare Tricia and her younger sisters in case she died) at a young age how to cook and bake and she makes what I call gourmet dishes. Chicken and dumplings might be my favorite thing she makes. Others love her "Tricia Bars" which is a dessert that is often requested and a recipe she doesn't mind sharing. (See back of the book matter for this special treat.)

My sixtieth birthday fell right before the COVID-19 pandemic was in full force. It hadn't yet been regularly talked about and we didn't think anything about having people over to our house at the time. We hosted a party with two dozen friends and family members to celebrate my milestone. Todd C. made it to my party, unexpectedly. He wasn't supposed to be there, and he and his wife came in just in time.

One of my sisters-in-law gave me a poster with facts from the year I was born. It was interesting to find out that in 1960, the first credit card was used, the Etch-A-Sketch was introduced, Trident gum was made available, new homes cost $12,700, new cars sold for $2,600, the U.S. postage stamp cost four cents, "The Price is Right" appeared on TV and "It's Now or Never" was released by Elvis Presley. My how times have changed.

Tricia turned sixty in July. This year is also the year we celebrated our fortieth anniversary. We travelled to Mazatlan for our honeymoon, Cozumel twenty years later and we were going to go to Cancun to celebrate this year, but there was a travel advisory and then a travel ban from both the CDC and the State Department. We paid for travel insurance that would refund air, hotel and meals "for any reason" but the third-party travel agency did not want to honor that. Luckily, our bank of more than thirty years decided to represent us, and they finally came through on the refund. So our anniversary trip has officially been postponed.

When the girls were younger, we would tent camp, and had been known to pitch a tent in the backyard a time or two. As we got older, we'd rent cabins. I still enjoy these getaways.

Again, when Tricia's father wrote to us and asked us to move back to the Denver area to be near family, we did so and stayed close. He got his wish and we were able to visit regularly. Until her parents passed away (both at age ninety-three), we lived only a mile from their home. My parents live a mile in the other direction, which has also been a blessing. It has been nice being so close to family over the years. My parents need more help as they have gotten older and I go over regularly and assist where I can.

As I have mentioned, my BD causes me to make impulsive decisions. Giving away my paintings was one of those impulses: I had them given away practically before the paint was dry. Remember, I impulsively got an ear pierced once and a tattoo on my left shoulder of the sock and buskin (comedy and tragedy) masks. The right shoulder has a tattoo of my family crest/coat of arms.

At nighttime, we typically watch both the local and national news for a half-hour each. My psychiatrist has encouraged me to limit my time watching news because of my stress reaction to COVID and BLM..

I am frequently unable to stay in the room during commercials when not doing well. I will turn on the outside flood lights at dark and lock all of the doors at bedtime (often checking and rechecking each door if relapsed).

There's no doubting BD affects my daily routine, despite trying to live as normally as I possibly can.

Chapter Twenty-One

Making a Connection:
Roles as a Therapist and Patient

At one time I was called an expert on addictions and provided therapy to those with mental illnesses. Now I'm on the other side of the desk, theoretically on "the couch," as a patient with my own diagnoses. For over thirty years, I had a career helping people with mental illness and now I've become that person.

I have been involuntarily admitted to the hospital because people think I'm a danger to myself. But as a licensed professional, I was admitting people to the hospital myself. The parallels of a mental health professional having mental health issues are wild and hard to understand. I would have therapists tell me things or make diagnoses and I already knew what they were telling me.

I've never wanted to be a difficult patient but have come across as such at times because I already knew what was happening to me. My compliancy makes me different from my brother.

The NIH states that 43 percent of people with BD will attempt suicide. Knowing I am one of those numbers is often a hard pill to swallow, no pun intended. Twelve percent of people with BD complete suicide. Knowing my brother Scott fell into this statistic is also very real and hard. NIH states that over 90 percent of patients with BD experience at least one relapse during their lifetime.

Many famous and creative people publicly live (or lived) with BD including Mariah Carey, Mel Gibson, Demi Lovato, Frank Sinatra, Ernest Hemingway and Winston Churchill. It's uplifting to be in the company of some amazing people, famous or not.

Relapses happen, unfortunately, as I have mentioned, and I do my best to deal. We take the ups with the downs and do our best to regulate.

Postscript

Providing Therapy in Today's Society

At the time of admission, an addiction client often asks for a counselor who has a personal history of substance abuse or dependence. They feel strongly that other providers would never understand what they are going through, and as a result their experience in treatment would be less effective.

Some programs agree with this approach as long as the applicant has a certain period of sobriety, specifically listing it in the job advertisement or discussing the preference or requirement in the job interview.

With that being said, is it, or should it be different in mental health (with psychiatric conditions)? There are peer counselors. These providers often work at agencies with chronically mentally ill clients who are stable. First, the counselors must complete training on basic counseling skills. They are also closely supervised.

During the global pandemic in 2020, my state's legislature and Governor passed and signed the bills respectively, which became laws. This allowed the Colorado Department of Regulatory Agencies (DORA) to reach out to me and all other previously certified and licensed mental health counselors and therapists who were retired or semi-retired and whose credentials had lapsed (or expired).

As long as we were working in good standing (no grievances against us) at the time of retirement, the correspondence stated that we could be reinstated to serve as mental health providers for essential workers, patients, and their families who are experiencing stress reactions ("Adjustment Disorders") related to COVID.

Even with my PTSD diagnosis, I have not signed up to work again. Should I? Would you if you were in my shoes?

Staying focused and keeping our sights on attainable goals can be lifesaving information for someone who has chronic mental illnesses like me. Because of its importance, it bears repeating. Prevent yourself from falling far down to the ground when depressed. Prevent yourself from bouncing high to the ceiling when manic. Prevent severe mood swings by maintaining yourself and walking steadily on the wire. If you are like me, you may be able to achieve this by balancing your mental health with both medications and psychotherapy. Always remember you are not alone.

The wire may have its ups and downs, but there are people who can help you when the waves are too strong, or you go too high or too low.

Be sure to reach out while you walk the wire.

"Tricia Bars"

Special recipe from Tricia Kannenberg

Ingredients:

32 caramels

5 Tbsp. cream

1 cup flour

1 cup quick oats

3/4 cup brown sugar

1/2 cup chopped pecans

1/2 tsp soda

1/4 tsp salt

3/4 cup butter, melted

1-6 oz. package chocolate chips

Directions:

Melt caramels with cream in a double-boiler or microwave. Combine flour, oats, brown sugar, soda, salt and butter. Press 3/4 of this mixture into a well-greased 11x7 inch pan. Bake in a 350-degree oven for 10 minutes. Spread chocolate chips and pecans over baked crumb mixture. Pour caramel over top and sprinkle with remaining crumbs.

Bake in a 350-degree oven for 15-20 minutes. Chill for 2 hours and cut into 24 bars. Enjoy!

Acknowledgments

Special thanks to the following people (associates, assistants, family members, friends, and treatment providers) for their assistance, unconditional support, and encouragement.

Tricia Kannenberg, SLP (Wife)

Corrie Kannenberg, Ph.D. (ABD) (Eldest daughter)

Leslie (Kannenberg) Heguy, MSN, FNP-C (Youngest daughter)

Vince Heguy (Son-in-law)

Nancy Kannenberg (Mother)

Herm Kannenberg (Father)

Kelly Kannenberg RTC (Younger sister)

Larry Miller, Ph.D. (Uncle and Godfather)

Jean Reiken (Sister-in-law)

Cristy Heim (Sister-in-law)

Ryan Kramer, M.D. (Family physician for 33 years)

Robert Kleinman, M.D. (Psychiatrist for 10 years until retirement)

Cynthia Dafler, M.D.; Loretta Riley, M.D. (Psychiatrists)

Carolyn Stoloff, Ph.D. (Therapist for 13 years until retirement)

Adam Maher, Psy.D. (Therapist)

Margie Carlin, C.T.R.S. (Group leader)

Don DeGroot, Ph.D. (Coworker for 5 years and longtime friend)

Michael Cummings, Ph.D. (College professor and longtime friend)

Scott DeMuro, Ph.D. (Former employer and longtime friend)

Tom Colburn (Pilot. Commander. Friend since childhood)

Jay Gross (Former coworker/support group facilitator for 5 years and longtime friend)

Doug Erler, M.A. (Former supervisor, employer, and longtime friend)

Joy Muratsuchi, R.N. (Longtime friend)

Hakim Janah (Longtime friend)

Ashley Basta, J.D. (Longtime friend)

Zach Dunlop, M.A. (Longtime friend)

Justin Winkler, EMT (Former coworker and longtime friend)

Juanita Vargas, Barber (and bimonthly "therapist")

About the Author

Little did he know that even as a thirty-year so-called "expert" in his field, Rand L. Kannenberg would later be diagnosed with four persistent and severe diagnoses: Bipolar I Disorder, Post Traumatic Stress Disorder (PTSD), Obsessive-Compulsive Disorder (OCD), and Generalized Anxiety Disorder (GAD). Once a therapist and trainer, Kannenberg is now a patient with numerous psychiatric admissions for danger to self (major attempts to commit suicide), confusion, or psychosis. He meets with a psychiatrist for medication management, a doctoral-level psychologist for therapy, and a group for support. He received ECT twelve times in the past and currently takes numerous medications.

To help prevent relapse and rearrest of parolees, probationers, work release inmates, and other criminal offenders at a community mental health center in 1986, Kannenberg's first book, "Sociotherapy for Sociotherapy: Resocial Group" (PESI Healthcare, Eau Claire, WI, 2003) outlines an evidence-based, twenty-four session group treatment program created for adult clients with the coexisting or co-occurring diagnoses of Substance Use Disorder (alcohol and/or other drugs, abuse or dependence) and the persistent problems of aggressiveness, breaking rules and laws, carelessness, dishonesty, impulsivity, indifference, irresponsibility and irritability (Antisocial Personality Disorder).

The contents of Kannenberg's second book, "Case Management Handbook for Clinicians" (PESI Healthcare, Eau Claire, WI, 2003) include the following: the differences between case management and social work, preventing unnecessary prescription problems, depression screenings, case manager attitudes with the chronically mentally ill, counseling and case management professional ethics, establishing rapport with providers, customer service and case management, avoiding case management burnout, hepatitis A/B/C screenings, HIV/AIDS screening, and TB screening.

Kannenberg's autobiography, *Balancing on a Tightrope: My Life with Bipolar Disorder* is a real account of a lifetime of struggle, loss and learning about the diagnoses that have become him and how he navigates life with his diseases.

Comments from the Author's Students

Reading this feedback is a part of my therapy when working on self-esteem. -Rand

"Your humor and ability to keep things moving with learning goals. Nobody even wanted to leave early, and you make hard work fun. Rand, you are a superb trainer-and your clinical skills are excellent. Great role model. BRAVO!"

(Kate Speck, Ph.D., Medical Education Director, Lincoln, Nebraska)

"The course provides a much-needed new interaction approach toward achieving a high rate of resocialization of a hard to reach group..."

(Professor Elia Vega, Mercedita, Puerto Rico)

"The course was excellent, practical and highly relevant. Rand communicated all aspects very well and was brilliant in putting all students at ease and eliciting their involvement."

(Lynette Todkill, University of Port Elizabeth, South Africa)

"This is a fascinating aspect of the criminal justice system. Rand is a walking wealth of knowledge, and versatile, very funny."

(Honorable Frederick Arnold, Municipal Court Judge, Portales, New Mexico)

"New group tools to help clients have a life. Wonderful humor, Rand...Wish I was taught more like this in school, as I feel I have really learned something that will help me be of service to others."

(Maggy Day, Counselor, Weott, California)

"This was one of the best seminars that I have attended in years and Rand was an excellent presenter. I am recommending this seminar to my colleagues."

(Lisa Barnes, Counselor, Cheyenne, Wyoming)

"Mr. Kannenberg has a marvelous, witty style. He kept my attention the whole day. Very informative."

(Sharon Hess-Witucki, Therapist, Northridge, California)

Other Books by Rand L. Kannenberg

Sociotherapy for Sociopaths (PESI Healthcare, 2003)

"Kannenberg's fresh approach to treating psychoactive chemical abusing sociopaths should be in every counselor's arsenal when treating a client of this nature." - Misti Storie, Education and Training Coordinator, Counselor Resources, "Reader's Corner," (NAADAC News, August 2005).

Case Management Handbook for Clinicians (PESI Healthcare, 2003)

"Even if new to the profession or a seasoned veteran, this book is a helpful resource to all addiction counselors...An addiction treatment facility's library is not complete without this book." - Misti Storie, Education and Training Coordinator,

Counselor Resources, "Reader's Corner," (NAADAC News, August 2005).

Connect with the Author

Facebook Page:

www.facebook.com/rand.leslie.kannenberg

Facebook Group:

www.facebook.com/groups/823140411156136

E-mail: randkannenberg@gmail.com

Publisher's Note:
With a few exceptions, the names of people and places have been changed and most prescription drug names left out intentionally. This work, as with all memoir and autobiographical works, is from the narrator's point of view and could be interpreted differently by others as they experienced it. People, places and timelines may have been altered for the sake of events of the story.